6th Grade

D1299014

IMPORTANT!
Instructions for Parents

- To use Summer Math Skills Sharpener, simply tear off a page and have your child complete it. The book is designed to be used *3-4 days per week for 10 weeks.*
- Our math books now support the Common Core Curriculum and the Standards of all 50 states. Therefore, some materials may not have been presented to your child. Please allow your child to skip concepts not yet learned. Introduce new concepts only if your child shows readiness.
- Check answers immediately for optimal feedback. An answer sheet and solution pages are provided at the back of the book. (**Solution pages represent only ONE method of solving each problem.**) A Lesson Tracker has been added for your convenience.
- "Help Pages" have been added at the front of the book to clarify certain concepts.
- Allow your child to use a calculator only for those problems marked "Calculator Skill."
- When solving division problems with remainders, students should use fractions or decimals rounded off to the nearest hundredth.
- When solving fraction problems, students should reduce answers to the lowest possible terms.
- Pages entitled "Brain Aerobics" are located at the back of the book. Have your child complete one page per week for extra practice. The answers to these questions are on the back of each page.
- A "Glossary of Terms" and a "Table of Measurements" are at the back of the book.
- Adjust the program to vacations, etc. Presentation of mixed concepts on every page ensures that all skills are reinforced; therefore, pages may be completed in any order.
- If your child experiences difficulty with concepts that have been already taught, address the problem with his or her teacher in the fall; more consistent problems indicate that a tutor may be needed.

We appreciate your comments. Please send in the enclosed evaluation page before November 1st, after your child has returned to school in the fall and you are able to determine the success of the Summer Math Skills Sharpener.

Dear Customer,

Every effort has been made to ensure the quality of this product. If any pages are missing or unclear, please call us at 1-800-411-8186 and we will be happy to send replacement pages.

Our commitment is to provide a product that is in keeping with the current standards of the Common Core Curriculum upon which the curricula in schools across the country are based. Please note that states, school systems and schools may differ from one another in what concepts are taught in a particular grade level.

Summer Math Skills Sharpener books may include concepts, terminology, or graphics that appear unfamiliar to parents. Please be advised that everything contained in the books appears in texts and standardized tests used across the nation. Please feel free to call for clarification.

We hope that using the Summer Math Skills Sharpener is a positive experience for your child; however, many children may need a reward system to help them complete the book.

If at any time you are not pleased with the quality of our products, know that we guarantee 100% satisfaction or your money will be refunded within one year of purchase.

Thank you for your order, and again, please feel free to call us at 1-800-411-8186.

Parent Order Form

Phone, Fax and Internet orders placed by 3pm Eastern Time on weekdays, ship the same day. We do not ship on weekends or holidays.

- ***Phone*** credit card orders to **800-411-8186** Monday – Friday, 9 am to 5 pm EST
- ***Fax*** credit card orders to **800-280-9269**
- ***Mail*** orders with check or credit card information to our NEW ADDRESS: Summer Skills • 2921 Wilson Dr. NW • Grand Rapids, MI 49534
- ***Internet*** orders are placed at www.summerskills.com (a secured site.)

We do not sell or share our customer information.

Make checks payable to: **Summer Skills**

Billing Address

Name ______________________

Address ______________________

City ______________ **ST**_____ **Zip** __________

Phone (____) _______ - __________

Shipping Address (if different)

Name ______________________

Address ______________________

City ______________ **ST**_____ **Zip** __________

Name of Child's school ______________________

Credit Card# (M/C, Visa, AmEx or Discover) ______________________ **Exp** ________ **CCV** ________

Email ______________________

Please indicate the number of **review** books you are ordering:

MATH

- ____ Pre-K
- ____ Kindergarten
- ____ 1st grade
- ____ 2nd grade
- ____ 3rd grade
- ____ 4th grade
- ____ 5th grade
- ____ 6th grade
- ____ 7th grade
- ____ Basic Math Review for the Middle Grades
- ____ Prealgebra
- ____ Algebra 1
- ____ Geometry
- ____ High School (Geometry & Algebra II)
- ____ Math for Life

LANGUAGE ARTS

- ____ Pre-K
- ____ Kindergarten
- ____ 1st grade
- ____ 2nd grade
- ____ 3rd grade
- ____ 4th grade
- ____ 5th grade
- ____ 6th grade
- ____ 7th grade
- ____ HS Prep

____ **STUDY SKILLS SHARPENER**
(For students 7th Grade through High School.)

____ **SPANISH I REVIEW**
(For students who have completed one full year of Spanish at the middle or high school level.)

____ **SPANISH II REVIEW**
(For students who have completed two full years of Spanish at the middle or high school level.)

____ **FRENCH I REVIEW**
(For students who have completed one full year of French at the middle or high school level.)

____ **TOUCH THE FUTURE**
(Keyboarding for 3rd through 6th grades.)

Make checks payable to: **Summer Skills**

Total Number of books ________ x **$18** = ________

Shipping Cost (see chart below) + ________

Total Cost due to Summer Skills = ________

Shipping Chart

To expedite via UPS Air or to ship outside the U.S. call 800-411-8186

Standard Shipping	Media Mail Up to 8 Business Days	Fed Ex **2-3 business days	USPS Priority **3-4 business days	USPS Express Priority **1-2 business days	UPS Ground **2-5 business days
Order Amount					*** call for HI, AK & PR**
1 Book	$3.80	$6.99	$8.00	$26.00	$12.00
2-3 Books	$5.00	$8.20	$9.00	$45.00	$13.50
4-5 Books	$6.00	$8.20	$9.00	$46.00	$14.50
6-10 Books	$8.00	$13.15	$9.00	$60.00	$15.50
11 or more books	not available	please call	please call	please call	please call

*** Orders to HI, AK and Puerto Rico ship USPS Priority Mail. Call for other mailing options.**
**** Orders placed by 3pm EST on weekdays, ship the same day. We do not ship on weekends or holidays.**

To assist in our efforts to comply with changing sales tax laws, please enclose a properly executed sales tax exemption certificate if you are an exempt institution.

GRADE 6 & 7 HELP PAGES

ESTIMATION AND ROUNDING

To estimate means to make a good guess. *Rounding* helps you to estimate more easily.

You can *round* numbers by using place value.

To *round* 362 to the nearest hundred:

1st Step	Find the hundreds place: <u>3</u>62
2nd Step	Look at the digit one place to its <u>right:</u> 3<u>6</u>2
3rd Step	If the digit is 5 or greater, *round* up. If the digit is less than 5, *round* down 6 > 5 so *round* up. To the nearest hundred, 362 *rounds* up to 400.

When you *round* down, the digit in your *rounding* place stays the same.

Example: 334 *rounds* down to 300.

ROUNDING DECIMALS

You can round decimals just as you round whole numbers.

Using place value, find the place you are trying to round to.

Look at the digit one place to its <u>right.</u>

If the digit is 5 or greater, round up. If the digit is less than 5, round down.

After you round a decimal number, you drop the digits to the right of the place you are rounding to.

Example: Round 6.526 to the nearest hundredth.

1st Step	Find the hundredths place: 6.5<u>2</u>7
2nd Step	Look at the place to the right: 6.52<u>7</u>
3rd Step	7 is more than 5 so you round up and drop the 7. To the nearest hundredth 6.527 rounds up to 6.53.

GRADE 6 & 7 HELP PAGES

ADDITION OF LARGE NUMBERS

To add large numbers, it is important to line up the digits according to place value. To make this job easier, line up numbers using *periods.*

Periods

Three places in the place value chart make up a *period. Periods* are always counted from the right (from the ones column) of a number. *Periods* are separated in numerals by commas.

Example: 1 , 0 0 0 (ones period) 1 , 0 0 0 , 0 0 0 (thousands period, ones period)

Count three digits from the right, insert commas.

ADDITION WITH REGROUPING (Carrying)

It is a good idea to estimate before computing to see if your answer is reasonable.

Example: 163,597 + 90,443 (Estimate 160,000 + 90,000 = 250,000

1st Step

```
  1 6 3, 5 9 7
+   9 0, 4 4 3
--------------
```

Put in vertical form. Line up the digits according to place value.

2nd Step Add the ones. Trade if needed.
3rd Step Add the tens. Trade if needed.
4th Step Add the hundreds. Trade if needed.
5th Step Add the thousands. Trade if needed.
6th Step Add the ten-thousands. Trade if needed.
7th Step Add the hundred-thousands.

Problem should look like this:

```
  1   1 1 1
  1 6 3,5 9 7
+   9 0,4 4 3
-------------
  2 5 4,0 4 0
```

The *sum* is 254,040. The answer is in keeping with the estimate 250,000.

GRADE 6 & 7 HELP PAGES

ADDING DECIMALS

Adding with decimals is the same as adding with whole numbers except that it is necessary to use the decimal point to line up the numbers, and a decimal point must appear in the answer.

Example: 3.13 + 3.87

1st Step

```
   3.13
 + 3.87
 ------
```

Line up decimal points.

2nd Step

```
      1
   3.13
 + 3.87
 ------
    . 0
```

Add the hundredths. Trade if needed.

3rd Step

```
    1 1
   3.13
 + 3.87
 ------
    .00
```

Add the tenths. Trade if needed.

4th Step

```
    1 1
   3.13
 + 3.87
 ------
   7.00
```

Add the whole numbers.

SUBTRACTION WITH REGROUPING (Borrowing)

Before subtracting, decide if a trade is necessary. You need to trade if there aren't enough ones, tens, hundreds, etc.

Example: 315,422 - 6,567

1st Step

```
  3 1 5, 4 2 2
 -    6, 5 6 7
 -------------
```

Put in vertical form. Line up the digits according to place value (see "periods" on previous page)

2nd Step Since 7 > 2, make a trade. Subtract the ones.
3rd Step 6 > 1, make a trade. Subtract the tens.
4th Step 5 > 3, make a trade. Subtract the hundreds.
5th Step 6 > 4, make a trade. Subtract the thousands.
6th Step No trade needed. Subtract the ten thousands. 0 holds the place.
7th Step Subtract the hundred thousands. 0 holds the place.

The problem should look like this:

```
        14 13 11
    0  4  3  1 12
  3 1 5, 4 2 2
 -    6, 5 6 7
 -------------
  3 0 8, 8 5 5
```

The *difference* is 308,855

GRADE 6 & 7 HELP PAGES

SUBTRACTION AND TRADING WITH CONSECUTIVE ZEROS

Before subtracting, decide if a trade is needed. Sometimes you may need to trade with (borrow from) one or more zeros.

Example: 400 - 273

1st Step

```
  4 0 0
- 2 7 3
-------
```

Write in vertical form, lining up place values.

2nd Step

```
  3 9 10
  4̸ 0̸ 0̸
- 2 7 3
-------
```

0 < 3; a trade is needed. You need to trade (borrow) 1 ten from 40 tens. This will leave 39 tens and 10 ones.

3rd Step

```
  3 9 10
  4̸ 0̸ 0̸
- 2 7 3
-------
  1 2 7
```

Subtract.

To subtract with 3 zeros, simply follow the same procedure.

Example:

```
   6  9 9 10
   7̸, 0̸ 0̸ 0̸
 - 5, 8 6 4
 ----------
   1, 1 3 6
```

SUBTRACTING DECIMALS

Subtracting decimals is the same as subtracting whole numbers except that it is necessary to use the decimal points to line up the numbers. The decimal point must appear in the answer.

Example: 7.2 - 4.03

1st Step

```
  7.20  ←  Add 0 to hold the place.
- 4.03
------
```

Align decimals.

2nd Step

```
     1 1
  7. 2̸0
- 4.03
------
  3.17
```

Subtract. Trade when necessary.

MULTIPLICATION OF FOUR-DIGITS BY TWO-DIGITS

Students should know multiplication facts and be able to multiply by one and two-digit multipliers. When multiplying larger numbers, the procedure is the same. Multiply by ones; multiply by tens; then add the partial products.

Example:

```
   1,232   ←— multiplicand
 x    32   ←— multiplier
 -------
 ¹2,¹464 \
          >←— partial products
  36,960 /
 -------
  39,424   ←— product
```

MULTIPLICATION OF LARGER NUMBERS WITH A THREE-DIGIT MULTIPLIER

Example:

```
   2,366
 x   148
 -------
```

```
     2 5 4
   2,366
 x   148
 -------
  18,928
```

Multipy the ones:
8 x 6 = 48, trade the 4
8 x 6 = 48 plus 4 = 52, trade the 5
8 x 3 = 24 plus 5 = 29, trade the 2
8 x 2 = 16 plus 2 = 18, trade the 1

```
     1 2 2
     2 5 4
   2,366
 x   148
 -------
  18,928
  94 640
 236 600
 -------
 350,168
```

Multipy the tens:
0 is the place holder
4 x 6 = 24, trade the 2
4 x 6 = 24 plus 2 = 26, trade the 2
4 x 3 = 12 + 2 = 14, trade the 1
4 x 2 = 8 + 1 = 9

Multiply the hundreds:
zeros hold the places
1 x 6 = 6
1 x 6 = 6
1 x 3 = 3
1 x 2 = 2

Now add the partial products.

The *product* is 350,168

MULTIPLYING A DECIMAL BY A DECIMAL

To multiply decimals, treat them as if they were whole numbers, at first ignoring the decimal point.

Example:

1st Step

```
  0.16 <— multiplicand
x 0.04 <— multiplier
     ? <— product
```

2nd Step

```
  0.16
x 0.04
    64
```

Multiply as if the factors were whole numbers.

Then count the places to the right of the decimal point in both the multiplicand and the multiplier. This will give you the number of places to the right of the decimal point needed in the product.

3rd Step

```
0.0064
  4321
```

Add zeros between the decimal point and the product if needed.

Add: 2 places in the multiplicand
+ 2 places in the multiplier
4 places in the product

Count 4 decimal places from the right of the product to place the decimal point.

The *product* is .0064

DIVISION OF FOUR-DIGITS BY TWO-DIGITS

When the dividend and divisor are numbers with two or more digits, division becomes a step-by-step process.

Example:

```
                      ??     <—— quotient
divisor ——> 75 ) 2083        <—— dividend
```

1st Step

Round the divisor up (75 rounds up to 80) and estimate the number of 80's in 208. The answer is 2.

2nd Step

```
      2
75 ) 2083
    -150
```

Multiply the divisor by the quotient (2 x 75) if the product of those two numbers is larger than the dividend, try a smaller quotient.

3rd Step

```
       2
75 / 2083
    -150
      58
```

Subtract and compare the remainder and the divisor. If the remainder is greater than the divisor, the quotient tried is too small; try a larger quotient.

4th Step

```
      27
75 / 2083
    -150
     583
```

Pull down the next digit from the dividend (3) and repeat the estimation and subtraction process. (How many times can 80 go into 583?) The answer is 7 times.

5th Step

```
      27
75 / 2083
    -150
     583
     525
      58
```

Multiply the divisor (7 x 75), subtract the product from the dividend, and compare.

6th Step

75 is larger than 58, so the number left over is called the *remainder.* The *remainder* should be written as a fraction or decimal.

Example: As a fraction

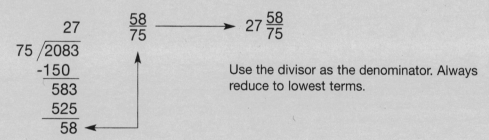

```
      27
75 / 2083
    -150
     583
     525
      58
```

$\frac{58}{75} \longrightarrow 27\frac{58}{75}$

Use the divisor as the denominator. Always reduce to lowest terms.

Example: As a decimal

```
      27.773
75 / 2083.000
    -150
     583
     525
      580
      525
       550
       525
        250
        225
```

27.773 ⟶ 27.77

Divide to the thousandths place. Round that number to the hundredths place.

The *quotient* is $27\frac{58}{75}$ or 27.77

DIVIDING DECIMALS

Begin dividing decimals the same way you would divide whole numbers.

Example:

1st Step

$1.5\overline{)6}$ ← dividend

↑ divisor

2nd Step

$1.5 \times 10 = 15$

↑ power of ten

Write the divisor as a whole number. Do this by multiplying the divisor by a power of 10 large enough to make it a whole number.

3rd Step

$6 \times 10 = 60$

↑ power of ten

Then multiply the dividend by the same power of 10.

It becomes

$$\begin{array}{r} 15\overline{)60} \\ \underline{60} \\ 0 \end{array}$$

4th Step

$$\begin{array}{r} 4. \\ 15.\overline{)60.} \end{array}$$

← Align decimal points

Now divide.

Another Example: $.036\overline{)7.2}$

$.036 \times 1000 = 36$

$7.2 \times 1000 = 7{,}200$

$$\begin{array}{r} 200. \\ 36.\overline{)7200.} \\ \underline{7200} \\ 0 \end{array}$$

ORDERING DECIMALS

If you know how to compare two decimals, you are then able to put a group of decimals in order.

1st Step

0.322
0.224
0.314

Line up the decimal points.

2nd Step	0.322 0.224 0.314	0.3 > 0.2, so 0.224 is the least.	Begin at the left. Find the first place where the digits are different. Compare.
3rd Step	0.322 0.314	0.02 > 0.01, so 0.322 > 0.314	Compare the remaining digits.
4th Step	Order from least to greatest: 0.224 ⟶ 0.314 ⟶ 0.322		

FRACTIONS

To work with fractions, you must be familiar with the terminology.

FACTORS – Factors are two numbers that when multiplied together form a product.

Example: 3 x 2 = 6

3 = Factor, 2 = Factor, 6 = Product

Every number except 1 has at least two factors: 1 and itself.

Example: 3 has only two factors: 3 and 1
6 has only four factors: 6, 1, 2 and 3

The *common factors* of two numbers are factors that they share.

Example: Common Factors of 6 and 18 (1, 2, 3 and 6)

① x ⑥ = 6
② x ③ = 6
① x 18 = 18
② x 9 = 18
③ x ⑥ = 18

The *greatest common factor* of two numbers is the common factor with the highest value.

Example: Find the *greatest common factor* of 12 and 36.

Factors of 12: 1, 2, 3, 4, 6, (12)

Factors of 36: 1, 2, 3, 4, 6, 9, (12), 18, 36

12 is the *greatest common factor*

MULTIPLES

To find the *multiples* of a number, multiply the number by other whole numbers. The list is infinite.

Example:

$3 \times 1 = \underline{3}$
$3 \times 2 = \underline{6}$
$3 \times 3 = \underline{9}$
$3 \times 4 = \underline{12}$
and so on

} Multiples of 3.

Some numbers share some of the same multiples. Those multiples are known as *common multiples*.

Example:

Multiples of 2	Multiples of 3
$2 \times 1 = \underline{2}$	$3 \times 1 = \underline{3}$
$2 \times 2 = \underline{4}$	$3 \times 2 = \boxed{6}$
$2 \times 3 = \boxed{6}$	$3 \times 3 = \underline{9}$

6 is a *common multiple* of 2 and 3

If we were to look for more *multiples* of 2 and 3, we could go on forever. Usually, we try to find the *least common multiple* (LCM) or the lowest number in value that is common to both.

Example:

Multiples of 2	Multiples of 3
$2 \times 1 = \underline{2}$	$3 \times 1 = \underline{3}$
$2 \times 2 = \underline{4}$	$3 \times 2 = \boxed{6}$
$2 \times 3 = \boxed{6}$	$3 \times 3 = \underline{9}$
$2 \times 4 = \underline{8}$	$3 \times 4 = \boxed{12}$
$2 \times 5 = \underline{10}$	$3 \times 5 = \underline{15}$
$2 \times 6 = \boxed{12}$	$3 \times 6 = \underline{18}$

The *least common multiple* (LCM) is 6 because it is the lowest number in value of all the multiples of 2 and 3.

LEAST COMMON DENOMINATOR (LCD)

When fractions have the same denominator it is called a *common denominator*.

To add, subtract or compare fractions, you must first find their *least common denominator*. This is the same as finding the *least common multiple* of the denominators.

Example: We already know that the *least common multiple* of 2 and 3 is 6 (see previous page). Therefore, the *LCD* of $\frac{1}{2}$ and $\frac{2}{3}$ is 6.

Now rewrite the fractions to make the denominators 6.

$\frac{1}{2} = \frac{?}{6}$ $6 \div 2 = (3)$ $\frac{3 \times 1}{3 \times 2} = \left(\frac{3}{6}\right)$

$\frac{2}{3} = \frac{?}{6}$ $6 \div 3 = (2)$ $\frac{2 \times 2}{2 \times 3} = \left(\frac{4}{6}\right)$

The fractions $\frac{3}{6}$ and $\frac{4}{6}$ can now be compared, added or subtracted.

IMPROPER FRACTIONS

When the numerator of a fraction is larger than or equal to the denominator, the fraction is called an *improper fraction.*

The value of an *improper fraction* is always greater than or equal to one.

Examples: $\frac{4}{3}$ $\frac{6}{5}$ $\frac{8}{8}$

Renaming

When solving problems involving fractions, the answer is never expressed as an improper fraction. Whether it be a sum, difference, product or quotient, the answer must be expressed as a whole or mixed number. This is called *renaming.*

Example: $\frac{4}{3} = 1\frac{1}{3}$ $\frac{6}{5} = 1\frac{1}{5}$ $\frac{8}{8} = 1$

If the *improper fraction* is difficult for you to *rename,* simply divide the numerator by the denominator and express the remainder in fraction form.

Example: $\frac{26}{10} = 10\overline{)26}$ → quotient $2\frac{6}{10}$; $26 - 20 = 6$

$$2\frac{6}{10} = 2\frac{3}{5}$$

Remember – *always reduce to lowest terms.*

SIMPLIFYING (Reducing) FRACTIONS (To Lowest Terms)

A fraction is in simplest form when its numerator and denominator have no common factor other than 1.

Divide the numerator and denominator by the greatest common factor

Example: $\frac{12}{18}$ Factors of 12: 2, 3, 4, (6)
Factors of 18: 2, 3, (6), 9

6 is the greatest common factor of 12 and 18.

$$\frac{12}{18} = \frac{12 \div \boxed{6}}{18 \div \boxed{6}} = \frac{2}{3}$$

COMPARING FRACTIONS

With Like Denominators

When fractions have the same denominator, compare the numerators.

Example: Compare $\frac{7}{10}$ to $\frac{5}{10}$

$7 > 5$ so $\frac{7}{10} > \frac{5}{10}$

With Unlike Denominators

When comparing fractions that have *unlike denominators,* find the *least common denominator*. Then make equivalent fractions with the same denominator and compare.

Example: $\frac{2}{3}$ compared to $\frac{3}{4}$

1st Step

Multiples of 3: 3, 6, 9, (12)
Multiples of 4: 4, 8, (12)

Find the least common denominator.

The *least common denominator* is 12.

2nd Step

$\frac{2}{3} = \frac{?}{12}$ $\quad 12 \div 3 = (4)$ $\quad \frac{4 \times 2}{4 \times 3} = \left(\frac{8}{12}\right)$

$\frac{3}{4} = \frac{?}{12}$ $\quad 12 \div 4 = (3)$ $\quad \frac{3 \times 3}{3 \times 4} = \left(\frac{9}{12}\right)$

3rd Step

$\frac{8}{12} < \frac{9}{12}$ so $\frac{2}{3} < \frac{3}{4}$

Now compare.

Comparing Mixed Numbers

To compare *mixed numbers,* first compare the whole numbers. If they are the same, compare the fractions.

Example: Compare $2\frac{2}{3}$ and $2\frac{3}{4}$

Now compare.

$2\frac{2}{3} < 2\frac{3}{4}$ because $\frac{2}{3} < \frac{3}{4}$ (see above)

GRADE 6 & 7 HELP PAGES

ORDERING FRACTIONS

If you know how to compare two fractions, then you also know how to order them.

Example: Order $\frac{1}{2}$ $\frac{3}{8}$ $\frac{3}{4}$

1st Step: $\frac{1}{2} = \boxed{\frac{4}{8}}$; $\frac{3}{4} = \boxed{\frac{6}{8}}$; $\boxed{\frac{3}{8}}$ Rewrite the fractions with the same denominators.

2nd Step: $\frac{3}{8} < \frac{4}{8} < \frac{6}{8}$ Compare the numerators.

so

$\frac{3}{8} < \frac{1}{2} < \frac{3}{4}$

ORDERING MIXED NUMBERS

To order *mixed numbers,* first compare and order the whole numbers. If the whole numbers are the same, compare and order the fractions.

ADDITION OF FRACTIONS

With Like Denominators

When you add fractions, check the denominators. If the fractions have *like* denominators, add the numerators. The denominator stays the same.

Example: $\frac{3}{8} + \frac{1}{8} = \frac{4}{8} \overset{\text{Simplify}}{=} \frac{1}{2}$

With Unlike Denominators

To add fractions with *unlike* denominators you must first make them equivalent. In other words, you must find the *lowest common denominators.*

Example: $\frac{1}{8} + \frac{1}{4}$

1st Step: $\frac{1}{8} = \frac{1}{8}$ Write as equivalent fractions with the same denominator

$+\ \frac{1}{4} = +\ \frac{2}{8}$ Now add the fractions

2nd Step: $\frac{3}{8}$ **The *sum* is $\frac{3}{8}$**

ADDING MIXED NUMBERS WITH LIKE DENOMINATORS

ADDITION:

Add the fraction; then add the whole numbers.

Example:

$$\begin{array}{r} 2\frac{3}{4} \\ +\ 2\frac{3}{4} \\ \hline 4\frac{6}{4} \end{array}$$

Rename if needed $5\frac{2}{4}$

$\frac{6}{4} = 1\frac{2}{4}$

Write in lowest terms

$$5\frac{2}{4} = \boxed{5\frac{1}{2}}$$

ADDING MIXED NUMBERS WITH UNLIKE DENOMINATORS

Example: $2\frac{1}{3} + 3\frac{3}{4}$

1st Step

$$\begin{array}{r} 2\frac{1}{3} = 2\frac{4}{12} \\ +\ 3\frac{3}{4} = 3\frac{9}{12} \\ \hline \end{array}$$

Write equivalent fractions with a common denominator. (See page 13)

2nd Step

$$\begin{array}{r} 2\frac{4}{12} \\ +\ 3\frac{9}{12} \\ \hline 5\frac{13}{12} \end{array}$$

Add the fractions. Add the whole numbers.

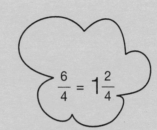

Rename if needed $5\frac{13}{12} = 6\frac{1}{12}$

GRADE 6 & 7 HELP PAGES

SUBTRACTION OF FRACTIONS USING LIKE DENOMINATORS

Subtract the numerators. The denominator stays the same.

Example: $\frac{5}{8} - \frac{3}{8}$

1st Step

$$\begin{array}{r} \frac{5}{8} \\ -\ \frac{3}{8} \\ \hline \underline{2} \end{array}$$

$5 - 3 = 2$

Subtract the numerators.

2nd Step

$$\begin{array}{r} \frac{5}{8} \\ -\ \frac{3}{8} \\ \hline \frac{2}{8} \end{array}$$

Write the denominator.

3rd Step

$\frac{2}{8} = \frac{1}{4}$

Write in lowest terms.

The *difference* is $\frac{1}{4}$

SUBTRACTION OF FRACTIONS WITH UNLIKE DENOMINATORS

Example: $\frac{2}{3} - \frac{1}{9}$

1st Step

$$\begin{array}{rcr} \frac{2}{3} & = & \frac{6}{9} \\ -\ \frac{1}{9} & = & -\ \frac{1}{9} \\ \hline & & \frac{5}{9} \end{array}$$

Write as equivalent fractions with a common denominator. (See page 13)

2nd Step

Now subtract the fractions.

Write in lowest terms if necessary.

GRADE 6 & 7 HELP PAGES

SUBTRACTION OF MIXED NUMBERS WITH LIKE DENOMINATORS

Sometimes you need to make a trade before you subtract with mixed numbers.

1st Step

$$\begin{array}{r} 3\frac{1}{4} \\ -\ \frac{3}{4} \\ \hline \end{array}$$

$\frac{3}{4} > \frac{1}{4}$

Compare the fractions.

2nd Step

$$\begin{array}{r} 3\frac{1}{4} \\ -\ \frac{3}{4} \\ \hline \end{array} \xrightarrow{\text{(trade)}} \begin{array}{r} 2\frac{5}{4} \\ -\ \frac{3}{4} \\ \hline \end{array}$$

Trade (borrow) one whole for $\frac{4}{4}$, and

add the $\frac{1}{4}$: $\frac{4}{4} + \frac{1}{4} = \frac{5}{4}$

So: $3\frac{1}{4}$ becomes $2\frac{5}{4}$

3rd Step

$$\begin{array}{r} 2\frac{5}{4} \\ -\ \frac{3}{4} \\ \hline 2\frac{2}{4} \end{array} = 2\frac{1}{2}$$

Subtract fractions. Subtract whole numbers.

Write in lowest terms.

SUBTRACTING A FRACTION FROM A WHOLE NUMBER

Example: $7 - \frac{3}{8}$

1st Step

$$\begin{array}{r} 7 \\ -\ \frac{3}{8} \\ \hline \end{array} \xrightarrow{\text{(trade)}} \begin{array}{r} 6\frac{8}{8} \\ -\ \frac{3}{8} \\ \hline \end{array}$$

Trade (borrow) one whole using same denominator as the fraction. 7 becomes $6\frac{8}{8}$.

2nd Step

$$\begin{array}{r} 6\frac{8}{8} \\ -\ \frac{3}{8} \\ \hline 6\frac{5}{8} \end{array}$$

Subtract fractions. Subtract whole numbers.

Simplify if necessary.

SUBTRACTING MIXED NUMBERS WITH UNLIKE DENOMINATORS

Example: $16\frac{9}{10} - 4\frac{1}{2}$

1st Step

$$16\frac{9}{10} = 16\frac{9}{10}$$

$$-\ 4\frac{1}{2} = 4\frac{5}{10}$$

Write equivalent fractions with the same denominator.

2nd Step

$$12\frac{4}{10}$$

Subtract the fractions. Subtract the whole numbers.

3rd Step

$$12\frac{4}{10} = 12\frac{2}{5}$$

Simplify (reduce).

MULTIPLYING FRACTIONS

When multiplying two fractions: Multiply the numerators to find the product's numerator.

Multiply the denominators to find the product's denominator.

Example:

$$\frac{1}{2} \times \frac{1}{3} = \frac{1 \times 1}{2 \times 3} = \frac{1}{6}$$

multiply the numerators

multiply the denominators

*It does not matter if the denominators are like or unlike.

MULTIPLYING A MIXED NUMBER BY A FRACTION

To multiply a mixed number by a fraction, change the mixed number to an improper fraction (where the numerator is larger than the denominator), then multiply the fractions.

Example: $1\frac{3}{4} \times \frac{2}{3}$

1st Step $1\frac{3}{4} = \frac{7}{4}$ — Change mixed number to an improper fraction.

(Multiply the whole number by the denominator and add the numerator. This is now the new numerator.) Retain the denominator.

2nd Step $\frac{7}{4} \times \frac{2}{3} = \frac{14}{}$ — Multiply the numerators.

3rd Step $\frac{7}{4} \times \frac{2}{3} = \frac{14}{12}$ — Multiply the denominators.

4th Step $1\frac{2}{12} = 1\frac{1}{6}$ — Rename. Simplify (reduce) the fraction if necessary.

The *product* is $1\frac{1}{6}$

MULTIPLYING TWO MIXED NUMBERS

Follow the same procedure as multiplying a mixed number by a fraction but change both to improper fractions.

Example: $1\frac{1}{2} \times 2\frac{1}{3}$

1st Step $1\frac{1}{2} = \frac{3}{2}$ $\quad 2\frac{1}{3} = \frac{7}{3}$ — Change both mixed numbers to improper fractions.

2nd Step	$\frac{3}{2} \times \frac{7}{3} = \frac{21}{6}$	Multiply numerators. Multiply denominators.
3rd Step	$\frac{21}{6} = 3\frac{3}{6} = 3\frac{1}{2}$	Rename and simplify (reduce).

DIVIDING FRACTIONS

Dividing a Fraction by a Fraction

Example: $\frac{1}{2} \div \frac{1}{3}$

1st Step	$\frac{1}{2} \div \frac{1}{3}$ ← divisor	Locate the *divisor*. In a number sentence, the divisor comes after the division sign.
2nd Step	$\frac{1}{3}$ inverted becomes $\frac{3}{1}$	The divisor must be *inverted*. To *invert* simply means to turn the fraction upside down.
3rd Step	$\frac{1}{2} \times \frac{3}{1} = \frac{3}{2}$	Multiply the two fractions.
4th Step	$\frac{3}{2} = 1\frac{1}{2}$	Rename.

The *quotient* is $1\frac{1}{2}$

Dividing a Whole Number by a Fraction

Example: $2 \div \frac{1}{3}$

1st Step: $2 = \frac{2}{1}$ — Put the *whole number* in fraction form.

2nd Step: $\frac{2}{1} \div \frac{1}{3}$ ← divisor — Locate the divisor and invert.

$\frac{1}{3}$ becomes $\frac{3}{1}$

3rd Step: $\frac{2}{1} \times \frac{3}{1} = \frac{6}{1}$ — Invert the divisor and multiply.

4th Step: $\frac{6}{1} = 6$

Dividing a Fraction by a Whole Number

Example: $\frac{1}{3} \div 2$

1st Step: $2 = \frac{2}{1}$ — Put the whole number in fraction form.

2nd Step: $\frac{1}{3} \div \frac{2}{1}$ ← divisor — Locate the divisor and invert.

$\frac{2}{1}$ becomes $\frac{1}{2}$

3rd Step: $\frac{1}{3} \times \frac{1}{2} = \frac{1}{6}$ — Multiply the numerators and denominators.

4th Step: $\frac{1}{6}$ is in lowest terms — Simplify (reduce) if necessary.

Dividing a Mixed Number by Another Mixed Number

Example: $2\frac{1}{2} \div 2\frac{1}{4}$

1st Step — $2\frac{1}{2} = \frac{5}{2}$ and $2\frac{1}{4} = \frac{9}{4}$ — Change both mixed numbers to improper fractions.

2nd Step — $\frac{5}{2} \div \frac{9}{4}$ ← divisor — Rewrite the problem. Locate the divisor and invert.

$\frac{9}{4}$ becomes $\frac{4}{9}$

3rd Step — $\frac{5}{2} \times \frac{4}{9} = \frac{20}{18}$ — Multiply the numerators and denominators.

4th Step — $\frac{20}{18} = 1\frac{2}{18} = 1\frac{1}{9}$ — Rename and simplify (reduce).

More About Dividing Fractions:

You know the algorithm for dividing fractions. Let's look at why it works. Consider the problem $\mathbf{20 \div 5}$. You are asking the question, how many groups of 5 are there in 20? $\mathbf{20 \div 5 = 4}$. Answer, there are 4 groups.

Now, look at $\mathbf{1 \div \frac{1}{4}}$. You are asking how many groups of $\frac{1}{4}$ are in 1.

$\mathbf{1 \div \frac{1}{4} = 1 \times 4 = 4}$, but why? If this were a pie and each slice were $\frac{1}{4}$ of the pie, there would be 4 slices.

Suppose only $\frac{1}{2}$ of a pie is left. How many $\frac{1}{4}$ slices would there be?

$\mathbf{\frac{1}{2} \div \frac{1}{4} = \frac{1}{2} \times 4 = 2}$. There are 2 slices.

Consider a pizza cut into eight slices. Each slice is $\frac{1}{8}$ of the pizza. How many slices? 8, of course. Let's say that by the time you reach the pizza, there is only $\frac{1}{4}$ left. How many $\frac{1}{8}$ slices in $\frac{1}{4}$ of a pizza?

$\frac{1}{4} \div \frac{1}{8} = \frac{1}{4} \times 8 = 2$. There are 2 pieces left.

When you multiply a number by a fraction, here is what happens.

$$15 \times \frac{2}{5} = \frac{15 \times 2}{5} = \frac{30}{5} = 6$$

Notice, you multiply by 2, but divide by 5.

When you divide a number by a fraction, you do the opposite.

$$12 \div \frac{2}{5} = 12 \div 2 \times 5 = \frac{12 \times 5}{2} = \frac{60}{2} = 30$$ Observe, that $12 \div \frac{2}{5} = 12 \times \frac{5}{2}$.

PERCENTAGES

Percentages are ratios. The term *percent* means "one part per hundred."

Example: $30\% = \frac{30}{100}$

Every percent is really a fraction with 100 as its denominator. That also means that every fraction with 100 as its denominator can be written as a percent.

Example: $\frac{30}{100} = 30\%$

Percents can also be expressed as decimals.

Example: $30\% = .30$

Therefore, there is a relationship among percents, decimals and fractions.

Example: $30\% = .30 = \frac{30}{100}$

$17\% = .17 = \frac{17}{100}$

To Change a Fraction to a Percent

Divide the numerator by the denominator.

Example: $\frac{2}{5} = 5\overline{)2.00}$ → $.40$

40% — Then change the decimal to a percent.

To Change a Percent to a Fraction

Express it as a fraction and reduce.

Example: 40%

$40\% = \frac{40}{100} = \frac{4}{10} = \frac{2}{5}$

To Compare Fractions, Decimals and Percents

Change them all to decimals.

Example: Put the following in order least to greatest; $\frac{1}{2}$, .25, 35%

1st Step	$\frac{1}{2} = 2\overline{)1.00}$ → $.50$ $35\% = .35$	Change fraction and percent to decimals.
2nd Step	Now compare; .50 .35 .25	Compare the decimals.
3rd Step	Least to greatest; $.25 < .35 < .50$ so	Order.
4th Step	$.25 < 35\% < \frac{1}{2}$	Put in original form. Order.

INTRODUCTION OF A VARIABLE IN AN ALGEBRAIC PROBLEM

A *variable* is a quantity that can change.

Example: *x* and *n* are two common variables. Their values change according to the problem. In one problem *n* may stand for the number 3; in another it may stand for the number 53.

An *expression* refers to numbers and variables joined together using the operations of arithmetic.

When solving a word problem use the numbers given to you. Use a variable for numbers **not** given to you. Then write an expression that describes what's going on in the problem.

Example: I had 3 marbles: Bob gave me more marbles.

expression: $3 + n$
n represents the number you don't know.

You can also use a *variable* in other types of problems such as:

Subtraction: $n - 3$
Multiplication: $3n$ (write multiplication without the times (x) symbol.)
Division: $\frac{n}{3}$ (write division in fraction form.)

In each case 3 is the known quantity, and *n* is the unknown quantity.

When you evaluate an expression, you substitute a number for every variable in that expression. Then you can compute. See the chart below for examples.

Expression	**Evaluate if n = 12**
$n + 3$	$12 + 3 = 15$
$n - 3$	$12 - 3 = 9$
$3n$	$3 \times 12 = 36$
$\frac{n}{3}$	$12 \div 3 = 4$

An *equation* is a mathematical sentence. It always says that two expressions are equal.

When you *solve an equation* you find values for the variables that make the equation true. Sometimes there is only one solution, and sometimes there is more than one solution.

SIMPLE INTEREST FOR ONE YEAR

Money can be borrowed from a lender (bank) for a fee. This fee is called *interest.* The money borrowed is called the *principal* and the *interest rate* is the percentage of interest the bank charges.

To find how much interest you owe for one year, multiply the principal times the interest rate.

Example: Suppose you need to borrow $5,000 from the bank. If the interest rate is 9%, you can calculate how much you will owe the bank.

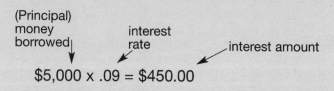

(Principal) money borrowed → $5,000; interest rate → .09; interest amount → $450.00

$5,000 x .09 = $450.00

$450.00 + $5,000 = $5,450 ← The amount of money to be repaid to the bank.

*Interest rates can fluctuate (change) from loan to loan.

ORDER OF OPERATIONS: Parentheses, powers, multiplication and division, from left to right; addition and subtraction, from left to right. (Use "Pretty Please, My Dear Aunt Sally" to help you remember this.)

Ex. $(9-1) \div 4 + 2 \times 3^2$

1. Parentheses: $8 \div 4 + 2 \times 3^2$
2. Powers: $8 \div 4 + 2 \times 9$
3. Multiplication and division, from left to right: $2 + 18$
4. Addition and subtraction, from left to right: 20

ALGEBRA LANGUAGE:

VARIABLE: A variable is a letter that can be replaced by a number.

Ex. $x + 8 = 13$ The x is a variable. In this case $x = 5$ (x is replaced by 5) makes this a true sentence. A variable can be a part of an expression.

Ex. $4x$ The x is the variable. Notice that in this case any value of x is allowed.

ALGEBRAIC EXPRESSION: When numbers and variables are joined by the operations of arithmetic, an algebraic expression is formed.

Ex. $2a + 5$

ALGEBRAIC SENTENCE: An algebraic sentence occurs when algebraic expressions are joined by a math verb. Math verbs are $=$, $<$, $>$, $\leq$, $\geq$, and $\approx$. Think of writing a math sentence as translating from English language to math language.

Ex. Three times a number plus 2 is 15. $3x + 2 = 15$

The opposite of a number is two times the number. $-x = 2x$

The cost (c) is greater than \$5.00. $c > \$5.00$

EQUATION: When two expressions are equal, the math sentence is an equation.

Ex. $5x - 8 = 12$

SOLVING ALGEBRAIC SENTENCES:

Think of solving an algebraic sentence as "unlocking" it. To do this you will perform opposite or inverse operations.

Ex. 1

$$x + 8 = -10$$
$$+-8 \quad +-8$$ **Add –8 (the opposite of 8) to both sides of the equation.**
$$x = -18$$

Ex. 2

$$2x = \frac{4}{5}$$
$$\frac{1}{2} \bullet 2x = \frac{4}{5} \bullet \frac{1}{2}$$ **Multiply both sides of the equation by $\frac{1}{2}$ (the inverse of 2)**
$$x = \frac{2}{5}$$

Another name for inverse is *reciprocal.*

Ex. 3

$$\frac{1}{2}x - 5 = 8$$
$$+5 \quad +5$$
$$\frac{1}{2}x = 13$$ **Notice that addition preceded multiplication.**
$$2 \bullet \frac{1}{2}x = 13 \bullet 2$$
$$x = 26$$

You might want to think about "unlocking" an equation as performing the order of operations in reverse order.

Ratio, Rate, Proportions, and Means-Extremes Property

Rate: Rate is a quotient. When x and y are quantities in *different units*, then x/y is the amount of x per amount of y. The word "per" means divide.

Ratio: Ratio is a quotient of x and y when they are in the *same units*.

Proportion: When two ratios or two rates are equal, they form a proportion.

Means-extremes: A convenient way to solve a proportion for an unknown number is to use the means-extremes property. It states that if $\frac{a}{b} = \frac{c}{d}$ then $ad = bc$. Your teacher may have called this cross multiplying or cross products.

Ex. 1: Show that $\frac{3}{4} = \frac{9}{12}$

$$4 \times 9 = 3 \times 12$$
$$36 = 36$$

Ex. 2: Solve for x.

$$\frac{3}{20} = \frac{x}{40}$$
$$20x = 120$$
$$\frac{1}{20} \bullet 20x = 120 \bullet \frac{1}{20}$$
$$x = 6$$

Ex. 3: Twenty pounds of cat food costs \$27.80. What is the cost, c, of 25 pounds?

a. Write the rate: $\frac{20\ pounds}{27.80}$

b. Write the proportion and solve:

$$\frac{20\ pounds}{\$27.80} = \frac{25\ pounds}{c}$$
$$25 \times \$27.80 = 20c$$
$$\frac{1}{20} \times 25 \times \$27.80 = 20c \times \frac{1}{20}$$
$$\$34.75 = c$$

More with rate

Suppose you have a rate in one unit and you wish to convert it to another.

Consider: You read an average of 25 pages every day. How many will you read in a month? (Use 1 month = 30 days)

$$\frac{25\ pages}{day} \times \frac{30\ days}{month} = \frac{750\ pages}{month}$$

Statistics:

A statistical question is one for which there are a variety of answers. The collected data can be described by its center and by its spread.

Measures of Central Tendency: There are three measures of central tendency: the *mean*, the *median*, and the *mode*.

Consider the data values 3 3 6 7 8 8 11 12 14

Mean: The mean is the average of a set of data.

$$mean = \frac{sum\ of\ data\ values}{number\ of\ data\ values}$$

$$mean = \frac{3+3+6+7+8+8+11+12+14}{9} = 8$$

Median: The median is the number in the middle when the values are ordered from smallest to largest. If there is an even number of data values, it is the average of the two in the middle. In the case above, the median is 8.

Mode: This is the number that occurs the most often. The data set has two modes, 3 and 8.

Statistics continued:

Mean absolute distribution (MAD): This is the average of how much data values differ from the mean value. A small MAD shows that data values are near the mean. A large MAD shows a wide spread of data. Here is how you find it.

In the example set , the mean is 8. Find the deviation (absolute distance) of each point from the mean.

$8 - 3 = 5$, $8 - 3 = 5$, $8 - 6 = 2$, $8 - 7 = 1$, $8 - 8 = 0$, $8 - 8 = 0$

$11 - 8 = 3$ $12 - 8 = 4$ $14 - 8 = 6$

The numbers 5, 5, 2, 1, 0, 0, 3, 4, and 6 represent the deviation of each number from the mean.

$$\text{The } MAD = \frac{sum\ of\ deviations\ from\ mean}{number\ of\ data\ values}$$

$$MAD = \frac{5+5+2+1+0+0+3+4+6}{9} = 2.\overline{8}$$

For this data set, the average spread from a mean of 8 is $2.\overline{8}$.

Interquartile range (IQR): Another measure of spread is the interquartile range. This is used with the median and is a measure of the middle 50% of the data. To find it, use the following steps:

We know the median is 8. The lower quartile is the median of the data values to the left of 8. In this case it is $\frac{3+6}{2} = 4.5$. The upper quartile is the median of the data values to the right of 8. $\frac{11+12}{2} = 11.5$. IQR = upper quartile – lower quartile. IQR = 11.5 – 4.5 = 7.

PLACE VALUE CHART

3,679,164,523,678.396528316546

6	trillionths (.000000000006)
4	hundred billionths (.00000000004)
5	ten billionths (.0000000005)
6	billionths (.000000006)
1	hundred millionths (.00000001)
3	ten millionths (.0000003)
8	millionths (.000008)
2	hundred thousandths (.00002)
5	ten thousandths (.0005)
6	thousandths (.006)
9	hundredths (.09)
3	tenths (.3)
.	
8	ones (8)
7	tens (70)
6	hundreds (600)
,	
3	thousands (3,000)
2	ten thousands (20,000)
5	hundred thousands (500,000)
,	
4	millions (4,000,000)
6	ten millions (60,000,000)
1	hundred millions (100,000,000)
,	
9	billions (9,000,000,000)
7	ten billions (70,000,000,000)
6	hundred billions (600,000,000,000)
,	
3	trillions (3,000,000,000,000)

1. Find the missing numbers.

$$\begin{array}{r} \square\,6\,3\,\square \\ +\,3\,\square\,4\,9 \\ \hline 5\,7\,8\,6 \end{array}$$

2. Evaluate and simplify.

a. $\frac{3}{10} \div \frac{3}{4} =$

b. $5\frac{1}{2} \times 2\frac{1}{3} =$

3. Mental Math: a. $700 \times 30 =$ ______________ b. $700 \times 60 =$ ______________

For problems 4 – 6, simplify. (Review the order of operations on the "Help Pages.")

4. $-7 + 7 =$

5. $4 + 3 \times 2 - 2 =$

6. $12 \div 3 \times 4 =$

7. Susan had four bags of candy, each weighing 6 ounces. Isabel had one bag of candy weighing $1\frac{1}{4}$ pounds. Which girl has the more candy in weight? Your work will justify your answer.

8. Round .5864 to the nearest:

a. tenth ____________ b. hundredth ____________ c. thousandth ____________

9. a. -5.8 is between the two integers ___________ and ___________.

   b. Round -5.8 to the nearest integer. _______________

10. How many times larger is the 7 in the number 7024 than the 7 in the number 427?

11. Evaluate and simplify.

a. $\begin{array}{r} 6\frac{2}{3} \\ +2\frac{1}{6} \\ \hline \end{array}$

b. $\begin{array}{r} 7 \\ -2\frac{3}{8} \\ \hline \end{array}$

12. Find a car for sale on the internet. Using the sales tax for your state, compute the cost of the car including sales tax.

13. *Rate* is a quotient. When x and y are quantities in different units, then x/y is the amount of x per amount y. (See "Help Pages")

    120 children read 960 books during "Reading Month" at school. Find the rate as books per child.

1. Evaluate and simplify.

   a. $2\frac{3}{4} \div 6 =$ b. $1\frac{5}{8} \times 4\frac{1}{3} =$

2. A *multiple* of an integer is the product of a number and any nonzero number

   a. Name the first four multiples of 3. ________, ________, ________, ________

   b. Name the first four multiples of 4. ________, ________, ________, ________

   c. The smallest common multiple of two numbers is the *least common multiple* or *LCM* of the two numbers. Find the least common multiple of 3 and 4. __________

3. Jon wishes to exchange $17.00 for quarters. He wants to know how many quarters he will receive. Write a math expression that will help him do this.

4. It took Caleb 9 hours to mow 4 lawns.

   a. Find his rate as hours per lawn.

   b. How long will it take him to mow 6 lawns?

5. Evaluate and simplify.

   a. $\begin{array}{r} \frac{11}{16} \\ -\ \frac{3}{8} \\ \hline \end{array}$ b. $\begin{array}{r} 5\frac{2}{3} \\ -\ 2\frac{1}{6} \\ \hline \end{array}$

6. 62.3 – 0.087 =

7. A *ratio* is the quotient of two quantities in the same unit. (See "Help Pages")
Aunt Margaret's chocolate cookie recipe uses 2 cups of walnuts for every 3 cups of chocolate chips.

a. Write the ratio of walnuts to chocolate chips.

b. How many cups of chocolate chips would you need for 3 cups of walnuts?

8. Find three fractions equivalent to $\frac{3}{4}$. ________, ________, ________

9. One out of every 20 people in the world is left-handed. If there are 34,960 people at a football game, how many could be left-handed?

10. Hands on: Here's how to find your hat size. With a tape measure, measure the circumference of your head where your hat would sit. Divide that number by $^{22}/_{7}$ and round to the nearest $^{1}/_{8}$ inch.

11. The Huron School Symphony Band needed 4 chaperones for every 15 students. How many chaperones did the band need for 180 students?

1. Use rounding to estimate the product: $295 \times 50 \approx$ ____________

2. Put these fractions in order from least to greatest:

$\frac{7}{12}$ $\frac{3}{4}$ $\frac{11}{24}$ $\frac{2}{3}$

a. ________ b. ________ c. _________ d. _________

3. Circle the set(s) which contain numbers that are multiples of both 3 and 4.

a. 12, 15, 24 b. 24, 36, 48 c. 12, 24, 60

4. a. Write in words: 80,000,000,000. ____________________

b. Write using scientific notation. ____________________

5. When two rates or ratios are equal, they are *proportional*. Which of the following proportions are true? (Hint: review means-extremes from the "Help Pages")

a. $\frac{1}{3} = \frac{33}{100}$ b. $\frac{1}{2} = \frac{8}{16}$ c. $\frac{4}{5} = \frac{21}{25}$ d. $\frac{5}{6} = \frac{15}{18}$

6. a. Name a pair of parallel lines. _______________

b. Name a pair of perpendicular lines. _______________

c. Name the point where line *b* intersects line *c*. _______________

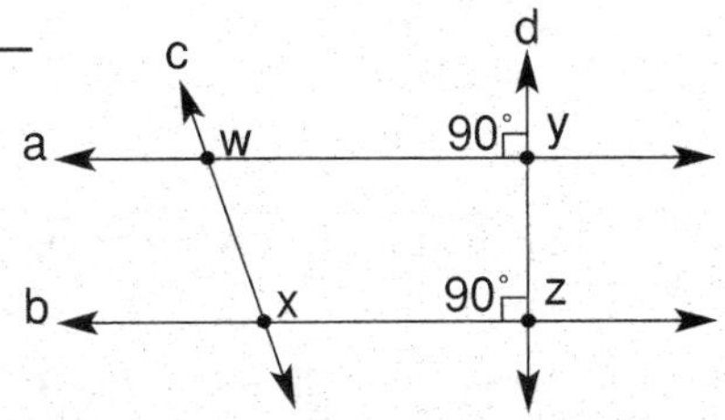

7. $92\overline{)5622}$

8. Evaluate the powers of 2.

2^0 ______ 2^1 ______ 2^2 ______ 2^3 ______

2^4 ______ 2^5 ______ 2^6 ______ 2^7 ______

2^8 ______ 2^9 ______ 2^{10} ______

9. A *variable* is a symbol that can be replaced by a number.

Let $a = 3$ and let $b = -4$. Find:

a. ab ______ b. $a + b$ ______

c. $a - b$ ______ d. b^2 ______

10. *Percent* means per centum or per 100. It is a ratio of a number to 100. When you see "per" think "division." Rename each of the following as a percent.

Example: $.45 = \frac{45}{100} = 45\%$ 45% is the ratio of 45 to 100.

a. .25 ______ b. .5 ______ c. $\frac{65}{100}$ ______

d. $\frac{3}{4}$ ______ e. $.\overline{3}$ ______ e. 1.0 ______

11. The area (A) of a rectangle with length (l) and width (w) is $A = lw$. Find the area of a rectangle with $l = 3$ in. and $w = \frac{1}{2}$ in.

Lesson #4

1. **An *expression* occurs when numbers and variables are combined using *arithmetic operations.* (addition, subtraction, multiplication, division, powers, etc.)**

   Let x = number. Write each expression.

   a. **Twice a number and seven** ____________________

   b. **Eight less than a number** ____________________

   c. **Number squared minus 2** ____________________

2. **You have $2\frac{1}{2}$ pounds of fudge to divide among four friends and yourself. How much will each person receive?**

3. **Name the points A, B, and C on the number line, l.**

```
                A   B           C
l <--------|-----*---*---------|-----*----|----------|-------->
          -1       -.5         0        .5          1
```

   a. __________ b. __________ c. __________

4. **Write in exponential form.**

   Example: $a \times a \times a \times a \times a = a^5$

   a. $2 \times 2 \times 2$ ________ b. -3×-3 ________ c. $y \times y \times y \times y \times y$ __________

5. **Hands on: Jamie has dimes and nickels. He has 3 more dimes than nickels. He has a total of $.75. How many of each coin does he have? (You can use coins to help you).**

   Dimes __________ **Nickels** __________

6. Evaluate and simplify.

a. $\frac{4}{9} \times \frac{3}{4} =$

b. $1\frac{2}{3} \div \frac{1}{3} =$

7. About 60% of the human body is water. How many pounds of water are in the body of a 95-pound child?

8. Lucinda has a coin collection. She sold 12 coins to a friend and bought 7 new coins. She then had 39 coins. How many did she have originally?

9. Mental math: $7\frac{3}{4} - 3\frac{1}{2} =$ ____________

10. Phone Service Plans:

Plan A	Plan B
800 minutes for $69 per month	$.13 per minute – no minimum

Which plan is better for the following two months?

May – used 750 minutes ___________

June – used 400 minutes ___________

11. A *factor* of a nonzero integer is a number that divides into the number with no remainder. Example: $20 \div 5 = 4$ with no remainder. 5 is a factor of 20. Find all the factors of 24. ______________________________

12. What is the least common multiple of 4 and 6? _____________

For problems 1-4, simplify.

1. $-(-3)$ 2. $7-(-2)$ 3. $-(-2)^2$ 4. $8-2(-2)$

5. **Rename each of the following as a decimal. Then rename each decimal as a percent.**

a. $\frac{1}{3}$ __________, __________ b. $\frac{1}{4}$ __________, __________

c. $\frac{1}{10}$ __________, __________ d. $\frac{17}{10}$ __________, __________

e. $\frac{9}{100}$ __________, __________ f. $\frac{39}{100}$ __________, __________

6. **Fill in the missing times in this sequence.**

4:00, 4:35, __________, 5:45, __________

7. **Identify the ordered pairs on the graph at the right.**

A = B =

C = D =

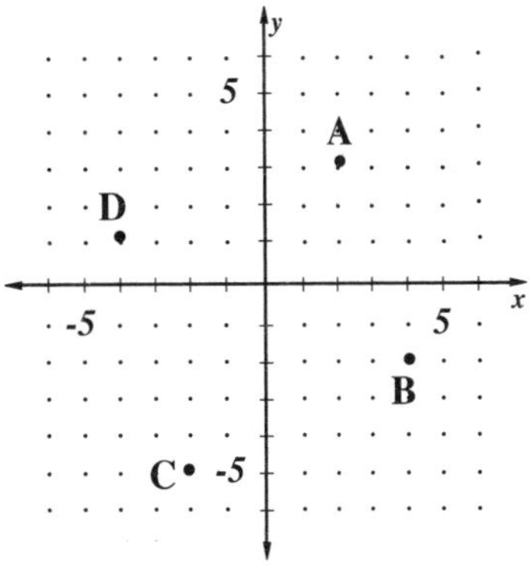

8. **Estimate:** $\frac{1}{3} \times 889 \approx$ ____________

9. Find the prime factors of each of the following:

   a. 30   b. 36   c. 27

10. Write these numbers in standard form.

   a. 30,000 + 200 + 40 + 6 ____________________

   b. 200,000 + 7,000 + 3 ____________________

11. Write the answers below in fraction form.

   a. 3 inches = __________ feet   b. 10 inches = __________ feet

   c. 18 inches = __________ yard   d. 2 feet = __________ yard

12. The first week Samantha learned to read Braille, she could read 10 words per minute. In the second week she increased her speed by 20%. In the third week she increased her speed again by another 25%. How many words could she read per minute by the third week?

13. $32\overline{)9826}$

14. Mental math: Tickets for the basketball district game are $6.75 each. If you have $30, how many tickets can you purchase?

1. a. $2.32 \times 4.1 =$ b. $30.5 \times 0.2 =$

2. List these numbers in order from least to greatest:

   2.19 2.91 2.9 2.099 2.01

   ________ ________ ________ ________ ________

3. Mental math: Estimate $253 \div 50 \approx$ ____________

4. a. Find three pairs of numbers that satisfy the equation $x + y = 4$.

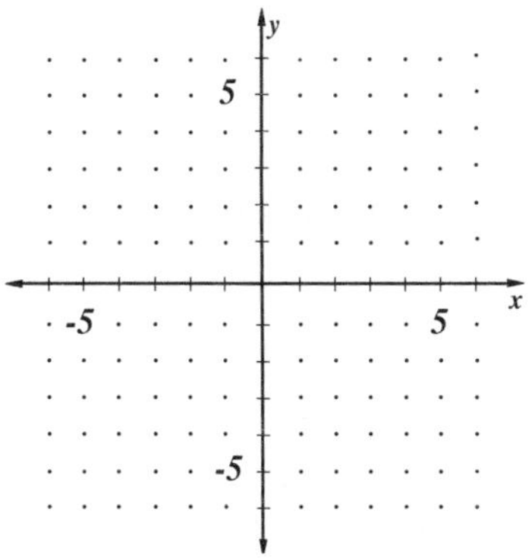

   b. Plot these points on the graph at the right and draw a line through them.

   c. Find another point on the line. Test it to see if it makes the equation true.

5. Gabrielle has $6\frac{1}{4}$ yards of fabric. She is making doll dresses. Each requires $\frac{3}{4}$ yard of fabric. How many dresses can she make?

6. The $\sqrt{12}$ is between what two whole numbers? ________ and ________

7. Round to the nearest hundredth. $4.6\overline{)68.11}$

8. a. If James weighed 8 pounds at birth, how much did he gain from birth to age one?

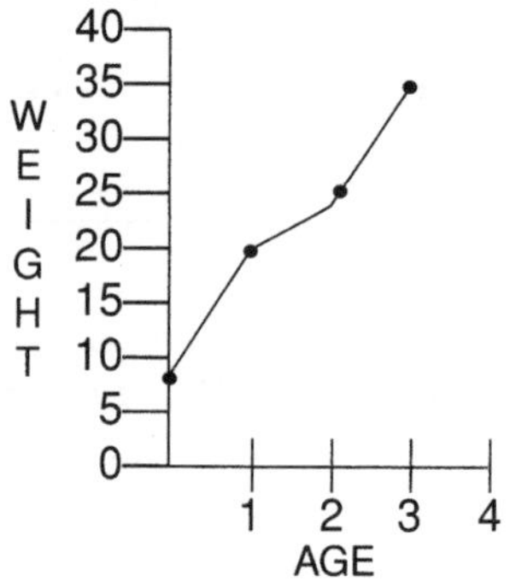

b. Between which two years did he have a 40% weight gain?

9. Evaluate and simplify.

a. $\begin{array}{r} 6 \\ -3\frac{3}{8} \\ \hline \end{array}$

b. $\begin{array}{r} 3\frac{2}{5} \\ +4\frac{1}{10} \\ \hline \end{array}$

10. a. Write the next three numbers (terms) in the pattern below.

6, 10, 14, ________, ________, ________

b. If the ninth term is 38, what is the tenth? __________

11. 234.81 + 23481 =

12. Choose the correct symbol (>, <, =) to make each sentence true.

a. .232 __________ .2318

b. $\frac{4}{5}$ __________ $\frac{5}{6}$

c. $\frac{1}{3}$ __________ .3

d. -2 __________ -3

e. 1.5 __________ 1.50

f. 200% __________ 2

1. Evaluate and simplify.

   a. $\frac{3}{10} \div \frac{4}{5} =$

   b. $\frac{5}{6} \times \frac{1}{3} \times \frac{3}{5} =$

2. The division sign is missing. Between which two numbers does it belong?

   3 0 7 5 2 5 = 123

3. Find the missing dividend. $52\overline{)}$ with quotient $15\frac{7}{52}$

4. What is the greatest common factor of 54 and 63? __________

5. What is the least common multiple of 6 and 9? __________

6. Put in order from least to greatest:

   0.3 -3 -3.3 $\frac{1}{3}$ .33

   __________ __________ __________ __________ __________

7. In 2011 the population of Mexico was 113 million.

   a. Write this number in decimal notation. ____________________

   b. Write this number in scientific notation. ____________________

8. The area (A) of a triangle with base (b) and height (h) is $A = \frac{1}{2}bh$. Find the area of a triangle with b = 2.6" and h= 1.3".

9. Everything in the store is discounted 20%. The original price of a bicycle is $229.

a. Find the new price.

b. If the sales tax is 6.5%, what is the final cost?

10. The histogram pictured to the right shows the points scored by the 6th grade basketball team for each game this season.

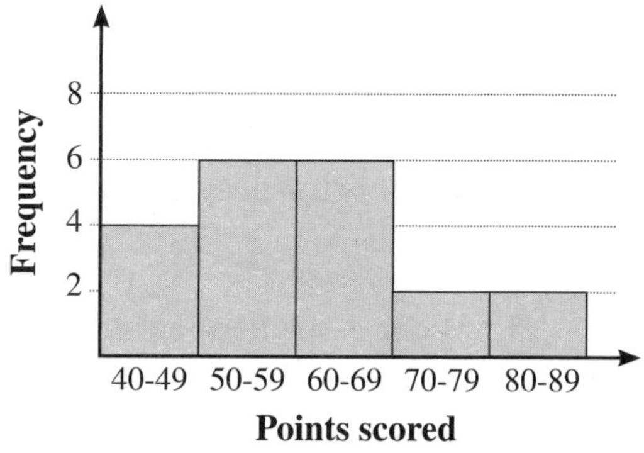

a. In how many games did they score fewer than 60 points?

b. They won every game in which they scored 60 or more points and one half of the other games. How many games did they win?

11. Mental math: Triple these numbers.

a. 30 ___________ b. 110 ___________ c. 50 ___________

12. Estimate the amount of a 20% tip on a bill of $39.00. ______________

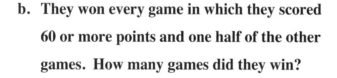

1. **Evaluate and simplify.**

   a. $\frac{3}{8} \div \frac{1}{3} =$ b. $3\frac{1}{2} \div \frac{1}{4} =$

2. **Use <, >, or = to make each sentence true.**

   a. $2+3\times4$ ________ $2\times3+4$ b. $3\times3-2$ ________ $3\times(3-2)$

   c. $6-2\times3$ ________ $2\times3-6$ d. $3-(3+3)$ ________ $3+(3-3)$

3. **In the language of math, "of" means multiply and "is" means equals.**

   30% of a number, *n*, is 6.

   a. **Write a math sentence (equation) to represent this situation.**

   b. **Solve your equation.**

4. **The *absolute value* of a number is its positive distance from zero. When an expression is within the absolute value symbols, treat them as symbols of grouping. Find each of the following:**

   Example: $|1-6| =$ **Think of this as follows: Evaluate** $1-6$ **first. Then find the absolute value.** $|1-6| = |-5| = 5$

   a. $|-5|$ b. $|2-5|$ c. $|2|-|-5|$

5. **The *mean* of a data set is the average of the set. Find the mean of the golf scores below.**

   98 100 88 89 95 90

6. Use the digits 6 0 8 0 2 to make the (a.) largest and (b.) smallest numbers possible. (Hint: You may use a decimal point).

a. ______________ b. ______________

7. A statistics problem generates a variety of responses. Which of the following are statistics problems?

________ a. The age of your teacher

________ b. The heights of the boys in your class

________ c. The number of hours of TV watched by your classmates last week

________ d. Your favorite number

________ e. The number of people in your family

8. Rename each as a decimal:

a. $\frac{3}{4}$ __________ b. $\frac{1}{3}$ __________ c. $\frac{2}{5}$ __________

9. A number and its *opposite* equal zero. Use the property of opposites to solve each equation. (See "Help Pages")

a. $x+7=3$ b. $x+(-8)=5$ c. $x+\frac{2}{3}=\frac{1}{4}$

10. Order these numbers from least to greatest.

-.21 $-\frac{1}{4}$ -.201 -17% $-\frac{3}{10}$

________ ________ ________ ________ ________

1. Evaluate and simplify.

a. $\begin{array}{r} 8\frac{2}{3} \\ -7\frac{1}{9} \\ \hline \end{array}$

b. $\begin{array}{r} 4\frac{1}{4} \\ +3\frac{5}{12} \\ \hline \end{array}$

c. $\begin{array}{r} 5\frac{1}{5} \\ -1\frac{3}{10} \\ \hline \end{array}$

2. What is the greatest common factor of 30, 45, and 90? ________

3. The area of a square lot is $\frac{1}{4}$ square mile. Find the length of a side.

4. Estimate: $29\overline{)3012}$

5. A *number sentence* is formed when two expressions are related using a math verb. You are acquainted with =. Other math verbs are $\leq$, $\geq$, $<$, $>$, $\approx$, and $\cong$. Write a math sentence for each of the following.

   a. 20 and a number, *n*, is less than 25. ____________________

   b. Twice Cooper's age, *a*, is greater than 10. ____________________

   c. An angle measure, *m*, is greater than $90°$. ____________________

6. Mental math: Change the order (*commutative property*) to find: $4 \times 17 \times 25$ ________

7. What number am I?

   a. My digits are consecutive numbers.

   b. The sum of my digits is 12.

   c. Two of my factors are 3 and 5.

   d. I am larger than 300 and smaller than 400.

8. a. Find the next three terms in this pattern.

   .253, .256, .259, .262, __________, __________, __________

   b. To get each next term, you add __________ to the previous term.

9. Complete the table of metric measures.

   a. 2000 cm = __________ m   b. 3000 g = __________ kg

   c. 100 mm = __________ cm   d. 4000 ml = __________ l

10. Label each of the following angles obtuse, acute, right, or straight.

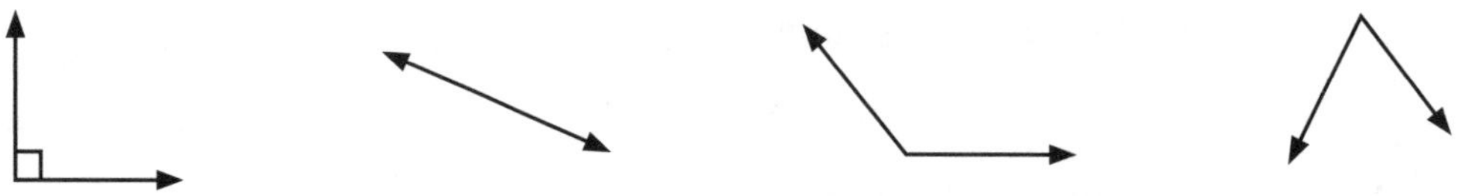

a. __________   b. __________   c. __________   d. __________

11. The formula for the area (A) of a circle with radius (r) is $A = \pi r^2$. Find the area of a circle with $r = 2.1$ inches. (Let $\pi \approx 3.14$) Round your answer to the nearest tenth.

1. Evaluate.

   a. $2.35 \times 100 =$ b. $.005 \times .01 =$ c. $4329 \times .0001 =$

2. Find two ways to determine the number of dimes in $8.70.

   Method 1:

   Method 2:

3. Suppose one Euro is worth $1.41 in the U.S. What is the better buy for a book, 8 Euros or $11.00 U. S? Your work will justify your answer.

4. Use the numbers below to write as many fractions as you can that equal $\frac{1}{2}$.

   5, 6, 7, 10, 13, 14, 20

5. When two expressions are equal, the number sentence is an *equation*.

   Jolie bought 3 hot dogs for $1.59 each and 3 orders of fries for x dollars each. She spent $7.74.

   a. Write a equation to represent this.

   b. Find the cost of one order of fries.

6. The formula for the Area (A) of a parallelogram with height (h) and base (b) is $A = bh$.

   Find the area of a parallelogram with $b = 4.5$ cm and $h = 3.5$ cm.

7. Complete the table of powers of 10.

   a. 10^0 ________ 10^1 ________ 10^2 ________

   10^3 ________ 10^4 ________ 10^5 ________

   10^6 ________ 10^7 ________

   c. When $n > 0$, 10^n is 1 followed by ________ zeros.

8. How many squares are there altogether?

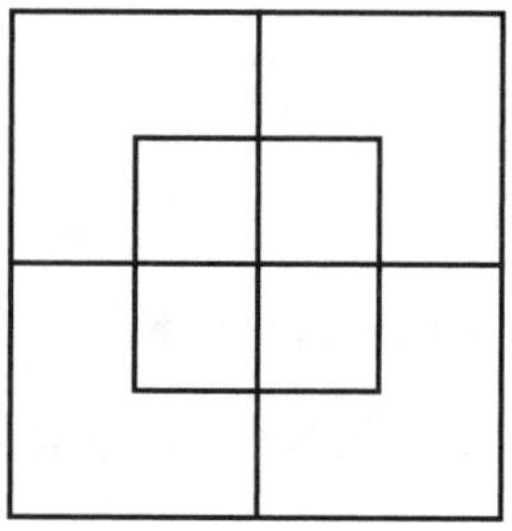

9. I am a number. When you add my two digits together, the answer is the same as when you multiply my two digits together. What am I?

10. a. Find three pairs of numbers that satisfy the equation $y = 3x$.

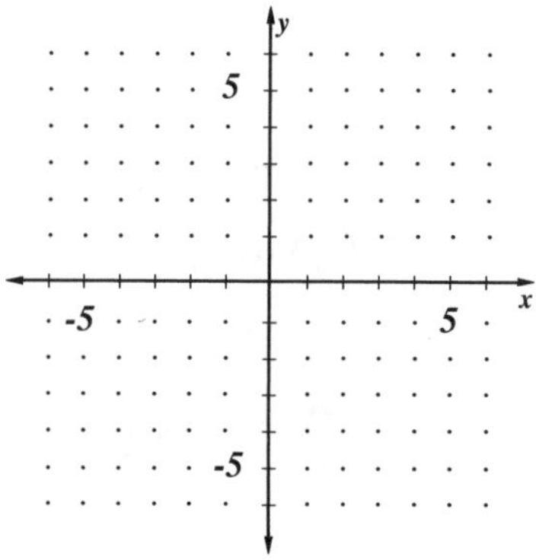

   b. Plot these points on the graph at the right and draw a line through them.

   c. (optional) *Slope* is the tilt of a line. It is the ratio of the rise over the run.

   Place your pencil on a point. Count vertically until you are even with the next point. This is the rise. Count horizontally until you reach your line. This is your run.

   The slope of this line is $\frac{3}{1} = 3$.

1. Evaluate.

   a. $426 \div 3.3 =$

   b. $.008 \div .04 =$

2. Grandma's car uses about 1.6 fluid ounces of gasoline per minute when the engine is idling. One night she parked her car and forgot to turn off the motor. She had just filled the tank. The tank holds 12 gallons. (1 gallon = 128 fluid ounces)

   a. Write the rate of ounces per minute.

   b. Write the rate of ounces per hour.

   c. How many hours will it take for her to run out of gasoline?

3. T or F: -2 > -5 ________

4. 3 km = __________ m = __________ cm = __________ mm

5. Find the missing numbers.

$$\begin{array}{r} 5\ 8\ 4 \\ -3\ \square\ \square \\ \hline 1\ 8\ 8 \end{array}$$

6. In January, the average temperature at the summit of Mt. Everest is -35° C. The temperature at base camp is -16° C. Find the temperature difference. ______________

7. How many $\frac{2}{3}$ cup servings of yogurt are in a $2\frac{1}{2}$ cup container? Explain how you found your answer. (See fraction division on "Help Pages.")

8. The Greenville sixth grade basketball team has played five games. Their free throw results are as follows:

	Shots	Successes
Game 1	11	6
Game 2	8	3
Game 3	8	6
Game 4	10	6
Game 5	11	10

What percent of their free throws are they making? Round to the nearest whole percent.

9. The distance from the earth to the sun is 93,000,000 miles. Write this number using scientific notation. ________________________

10. Consider the pattern below:

1 2 3 4 5

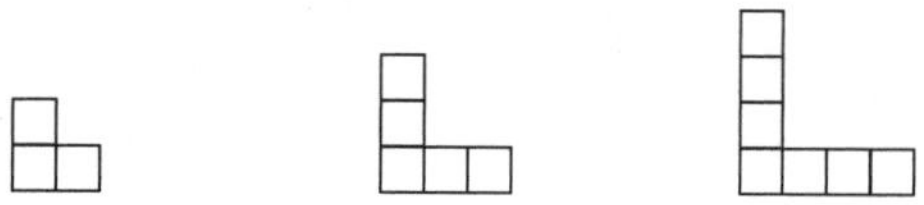

a. Draw the next two figures in the sequence.

b. Complete the table.

Figure	1	2	3	4	5
Number of squares	3	5	7	_____	_____

c. Without drawing it, predict the number of squares needed to draw figure 6. _____

For problems 1 – 3, simplify.

1. $2 - 3 \times 4^2 =$

2. $\frac{4-3}{6-2} =$

3. $(2+3)+6 \div 2 =$

4. Evaluate and simplify.

a. $12 \div \frac{3}{4} =$

b. $12 \times \frac{3}{4} =$

5. Write the answers in fraction form. A nickel is:

a. ________ of a dollar. b. ________ of a quarter.

c. ________ of a dime.

6. Order from least to greatest:

.0675 .0682 .0668 .0670

________ ________ ________ ________

7. Evaluate the perfect squares from 1 through 12.

$1^2 =$ $2^2 =$ $3^2 =$ $4^2 =$

$5^2 =$ $6^2 =$ $7^2 =$ $8^2 =$

$9^2 =$ $10^2 =$ $11^2 =$ $12^2 =$

8. The average number of cells in a human body is 10 trillion.

a. Write number in standard notation. ____________________

b. Write this number in scientific notation. ________________________

9. Mental math: Estimate the product of $25.027 \times 3.14 \approx$ ______________.

10. Mom's brownie recipe uses 2 cups of sugar and 3 cups of flour. The recipe makes 24 brownies.

    a. Find the ratio of sugar to flour.

    b. If you have only 1 cup of sugar, how much flour will you need?

    c. How much flour will you need to make 60 brownies?

11. The *reciprocal* of a number, n, is $\frac{1}{n}$. Find the reciprocal of each of the following:

    a. 2 _________ b. $\frac{2}{3}$ _________ c. –5 _________

    d. Multiply each number by its reciprocal. Conclude: $n \times \frac{1}{n} =$ _________.

12. The formula for the area (A) of a trapezoid with bases $(b_1 \text{ and } b_2)$ and height (h) is $A = \frac{1}{2}h(b_1 + b_2)$. Find the area of a trapezoid with $h = \frac{1}{3}$ ft, $b_1 = \frac{2}{3}$ ft, and $b_2 = 1\frac{1}{3}$ ft.

For problems 1 – 3, use the property of reciprocals to solve for x.

1. $\frac{1}{3}x = \frac{2}{3}$ 2. $4x = \frac{4}{7}$ 3. $-3x = 4$

4. $.05\overline{)3.675}$

5. Find the missing numbers. $\frac{\square}{200} = \frac{60}{100} = \frac{\square}{50} = \frac{\square}{25}$

6. a. Name the prime factors of 42: __________, __________, __________
   b. Name a common factor of 12 and 15: __________

7. In a class of 30 students, 16 are girls. What percent (p) of the class is girls?
   a. Write a math sentence to represent this situation.

   b. Solve your math sentence.

8. Order these numbers from least to greatest:

   $-\frac{13}{18}$ $-\frac{5}{6}$ $-\frac{2}{3}$ $-\frac{7}{9}$

   __________ __________ __________ __________

9. Which number does not fit the pattern below? ________
   49, 48, 46, 43, __________, __________, __________, 21
   a. 39 b. 34 c. 29 d. 28

10. Nine submarine sandwiches cost $47.25.

a. Find the cost for one submarine sandwich. (This is the *unit cost.*)

b. How much would you pay for 13 submarine sandwiches?

11. Isa has 30 feet of fencing with which to make a rectangular dog pen. Two sides each must be $8\frac{1}{2}$ feet long.

a. Find the length of each of the other two sides.

b. Find the area of the pen.

12. Marti has the following scores on her third quarter math tests:

89 94 65 100 98

a. Find her mean score.

b. Find her median score.

c. Assume a score of 88–92 is a B+ and 93-95 is an A-. What do you think her grade should be?

For problems 1 – 3, solve for x.

1. $3x-2=5$

2. $-5x+\frac{1}{2}=6$

3. $\frac{3}{4}x+2=11$

4. Find the missing number. $\square 4 \overline{)220}$ with quotient 5

5. Round these numbers to the nearest integer.

a. 5.87 ________ b. .96 ________ c. -1.7 ________ d. -.2 ________

6. Evaluate and simplify.

a. $5\div 1\frac{3}{8}=$

b. $1\frac{2}{5}\times 2\frac{1}{4}=$

7. Estimate to the nearest hour. You are driving 60 miles per hour. Your destination is 531 miles away. About how many hours will it take to reach it? ____________

8. There were 30 multiple-choice questions on your history test. You got a 90%. How many questions did you answer correctly?

9. Translate into a math sentence: *Three times a number is greater than 10 and the number.*

10. About what distance will you cover in one long step? __________

    a. 1 centimeter b. 1 meter c. 1 kilometer

11. a. Plot the points on the graph to the right.

    A= (-2, 4) B= (4, -3)

    C= (-2, -3)

    b. Connect the points in alphabetical order. Connect C to A.

    c. Identify the figure. ______________

    d. Find the area of the figure.

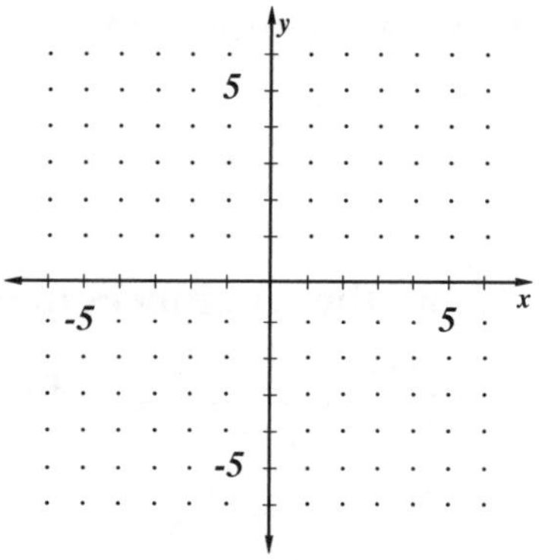

12. In 1989, it took space probe "Magellan" 15 months to reach Venus. The journey covered about 30,000,000 miles. About how many miles was that per day?

13. Let $x = \{0, 1, 2, 3, 4, 5\}$. Find the values for x that make this number sentence true.

    $x(5 - x) = 0$

Joke: Why is a meter too stubborn? Because it won't give an inch.

1. $.005\overline{)10.387}$

2. $43.2 \div 2.4 =$

3. Your favorite TV show starts at 8:00 p.m. It is now 6:02 p.m. You must attend a practice that will take an hour and 45 minutes and take a shower afterward which will take about 10 minutes. How much time have you allowed before your show starts?

4. Which of the following numbers is closest to $\frac{1}{5}$?

   a. $\frac{6}{29}$ b. .19 c. 20.1%

5. It took Ivan 9 hours to wash 5 cars. How many cars can he wash if he has 27 hours?

6. Write a story problem that could be solved using the following equation:

   $4\frac{1}{4} \div \frac{1}{2} =$

7. Let $x = \{-2, -1, 0, 1, 2\}$. Find the values of x that make the sentence true.

   $x^2 = 4$

8. Mental math: It costs $.15 per day to operate one 60-watt light bulb. How much does it cost to operate 10 similar light bulbs for 10 days? ____________________

9. a. Translate this sentence into a number sentence. *Twice a number and 5 is -4.*

   b. Solve your sentence.

10. On the number line show that $-2 > -4$.

←---→

11. The area of a certain rectangular parking lot is $\frac{2}{3}$ of a square mile. If one side is $\frac{3}{4}$ mile, what is the length of the other side?

12. On the map, the distance between Oklahoma City and Tulsa is $4\frac{1}{4}$ inches. If 1 inch = 25 miles, what is the distance between the two cities?

1. **Simplify:**

   a. $|-2| =$ b. $-|-2| =$ c. $-2^2 =$ d. $(-2)^2 =$

2. **Convert each of the following:**

   a. 24 in = __________ ft b. 64 oz = __________ lb

   c. 12 ft = __________ yd d. 6 qt = __________ gal

3. **30 is what percent (p) of 80?**

   a. **Write an equation to represent this situation.**

   b. **Solve your equation.**

4. **Ava babysits for $7.00 per hour.**

   a. **Complete the table to show her wage (w) per hour (h) worked.**

h =	1	2	3	4	5
w =	7.00				

   b. **Write an equation for her wage (w) in terms of hours (h).**

   c. **Graph this equation on the coordinates at the right.**

   d. **Use your graph to find her pay for 8 hours of babysitting.**

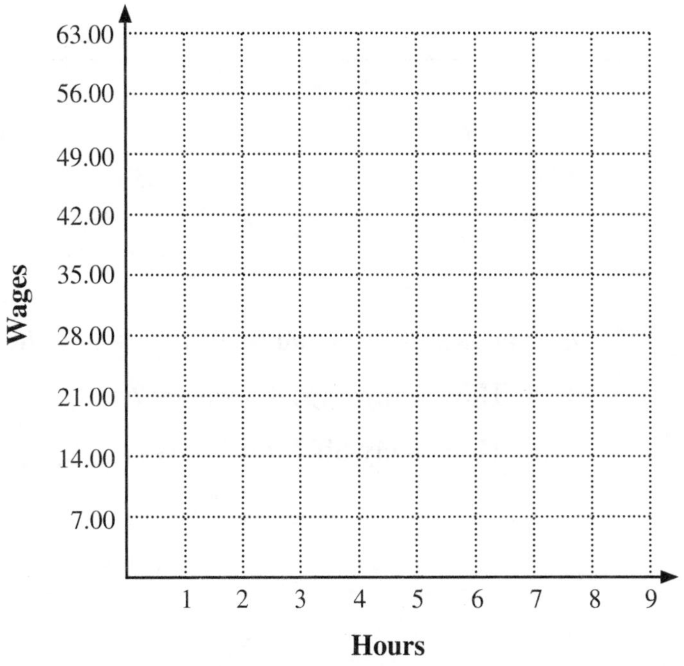

5. **Round 768423.967 to the nearest:**

   a. **thousand** _______________ b. **hundred** _______________

   c. **tenth** _______________ d. **hundredth** _______________

6. **Lilly has $4\frac{1}{2}$ pounds of fudge. She wants to divide it into $\frac{3}{4}$ pound packages to freeze.**

   How many packages will she have?

7. **Write in words: .000302** _________________________

8. **Fill in the missing ingredients in this recipe for 12, 18, or 24 cupcakes.**

cupcakes	flour	sugar	oil	eggs	baking powder	salt
12	2 cups	1 cup	$\frac{1}{2}$ cup	2	$\frac{1}{2}$ tsp.	$\frac{1}{4}$ tsp.
18		$1\frac{1}{2}$ cups				$\frac{3}{8}$ tsp.
24			1 cup		1 tsp.	

9. **Kadra saw dogs and birds in a field. She counted 28 feet and 8 heads.**

   a. **How many dogs did she see?** _______________

   b. **How many birds did she see?** _______________

For problems 1 – 3, evaluate and simplify.

1. $\frac{3}{4}+\frac{2}{3}\div\frac{1}{6}=$

2. $\frac{3}{4}-\frac{1}{4}\times1\frac{1}{2}=$

3. $\left(\frac{1}{2}\right)^2+\frac{3}{8}=$

4. **Rename each fraction as a decimal.**

   a. $\frac{4}{5}=$ __________ b. $\frac{3}{4}=$ __________ c. $\frac{2}{3}=$ __________

5. **Write these percents as decimals:**

   a. 14.3% __________ b. 200% __________ c. .002% __________

6. **The stem-and-leaf plot shows the weight (in pounds) of the students on the 6th grade football team.**

8	8 9
9	5 8 8
10	8 8 8 9
11	3 5 5 7 8
12	2 4 4 9
13	9 9
14	9

9 | 8 = 98 pounds

   a. How many boys are on the team? __________

   b. Which weight appears three times? __________

   c. What is the median weight? ___________

   d. A new boy, who weighs 140 pounds, joins the team. How will his weight affect the median?

7. One year the coldest temperature in Minot, North Dakota was -19° F. The hottest day the same year was 85° F. What was the numerical difference between the hottest and the coldest days?

8. Find the missing numbers.

a. $\frac{2}{3} - \square = \frac{5}{8}$

b. $.5 + \square = 1.2$

9. Mental math:

a. 125 + 275 + 120 = ______________

b. 500 – 150 – 25 = ______________

10. Match each shape with its area formula.

_____ rectangle　　a. $A = \frac{1}{2}bh$

_____ square　　b. $A = \frac{1}{2}h(b_1 + b_2)$

_____ trapezoid　　c. $A = \pi r^2$

_____ circle　　d. $A = lw$

_____ triangle　　e. $A = bh$

_____ parallelogram　　f. $A = s^2$

11. Write the calculator sequence to correctly evaluate: $\frac{4+8}{4-2}$.

For problems 1 – 3, solve for x.

1. $\frac{3}{4}x = \frac{12}{15}$

2. $-2x = \frac{1}{5}$

3. $x - \frac{1}{3} = \frac{5}{6}$

4. **What is the numerical difference between the boiling point and the freezing point of water measured in degrees:**

   Fahrenheit? ______________ Celsius? ______________

5. **What number am I?**

   a. **I am a multiple of 2.**

   b. **The sum of my digits is 7.**

   c. **The product of my digits is 12.**

6. **The cost (c) of jelly beans is \$1.39 per pound (p).**

   a. **Complete the table.**

$p =$	1	2	3	4	5
$c =$	1.39				

   b. **Write an equation for the cost (c) in terms of pounds (p).**

   c. **Use your equation to find the cost of 8 pounds of jelly beans.**

7. **Mental math:**

   a. $4008 \times 100 =$ __________ b. $4008 \times .010 =$ __________

8. a. Draw and label all the possible integer dimensions for a rectangle that has an area of 16 square units.

b. Which has the smallest perimeter?

9. a. Draw a square that is 1 centimeter on a side. Draw a second square that is 3 centimeters on a side.

b. Find the perimeter of each square. __________ and __________

c. Find the area of each square. __________ and __________

d. The perimeter of the larger square is __________ times that of the smaller square.

e. The area of the larger square is __________ times that of the smaller square.

10. The *interquartile range* (IQR) is a measure of deviation from middle. It is the range of the middle 50% of a data group. (See "Help Pages") Use the data below. Follow each step to find the *interquartile range*. This may be a new concept for you.

1 2 6 5 3 8 2 4 7 1 8

(1) Find the median. __________

(2) Draw a line through the median. Use the numbers to the left of the median. Find the median of these. This number is the lower quartile. __________

(3) Use the numbers to the right of the median. Find the median of these. This number is the upper quartile. __________

(4) *The interquartile range* (IQR) is the *upper quartile – lower quartile.*

IQR = _________

1. Estimate: $\frac{9}{10}+\frac{6}{7}=$ Is this sum:

   a. Less than 2?   b. More than 2?

2. Evaluate and simplify.

   a. $\frac{3}{5}\times 2\frac{2}{5}=$ b. $4\frac{1}{2}\div\frac{5}{8}=$

3. The surface area of a prism can be represented using a *net*. (All prisms have rectangular sides. They are identified by their bases, rectangle, triangle, etc. Think of a net as cutting a prism into rectangles and their base shape and taping them together).
   Use the net pictured at the right.

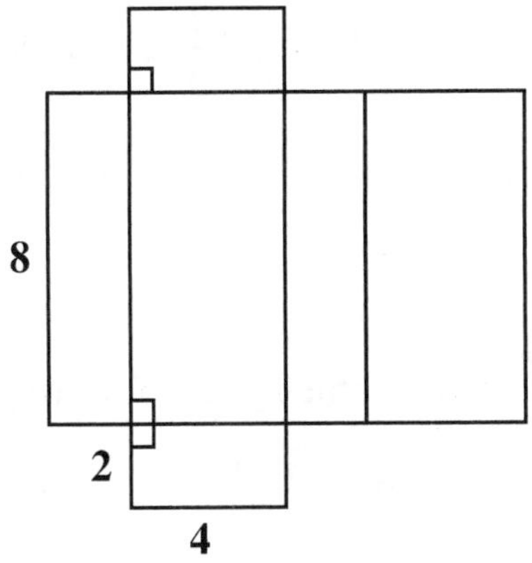

   a. Find the surface area of the prism.

   b. The volume (V) of a prism with rectangular base area (B) is $V = Bh$. ($B = lw$)
   Find the volume of the prism.

4. Match each figure to its description.

a. quadrilateral	_____	Both pairs of opposite sides are parallel.
b. kite	_____	One pair of opposite sides is parallel.
c. trapezoid	_____	It has four sides.
d. parallelogram	_____	All angles are right angles, and all sides are equal.
e. rectangle	_____	Two distinct pairs of consecutive sides are equal.
f. rhombus	_____	Opposite sides are equal, and all angles are right angles.
g. square	_____	All sides are equal

5. Is it cold or warm at 32 ° C? __________

6. Consider the number 957.821

   a. Which number is in the hundreds place? __________

   b. Which number is in the hundredths place? __________

7. Carter has a board 10 feet long. He is making baseball racks, each of which requires a board $1\frac{2}{3}$ feet in length. How many of these can he cut from his board?

8. Which of the following are less than 1?

   a. $\sqrt{2}$ b. 75% c. $|-2|$ d. -1.5 e. π

9. Find the area of the polygon pictured to the right.

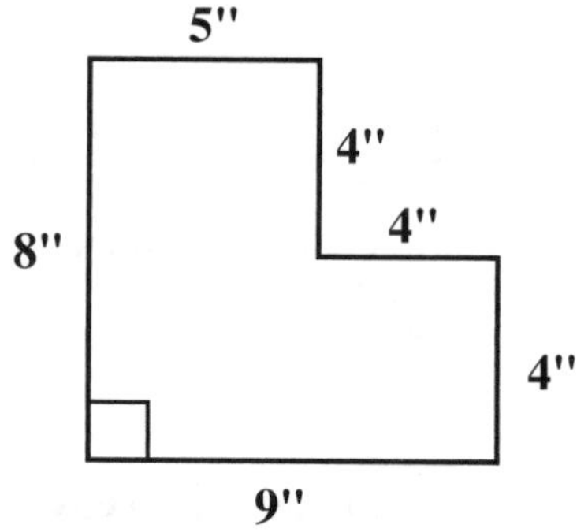

10. a. Complete the table below.

x	0	1	_____	_____	4	_____
y	11	8	5	_____	_____	_____

   b. What is the rule for finding each next y?

For problems 1 – 3, find the value of x to make the proportion true.

1. $\frac{x}{5} = \frac{9}{4}$

2. $\frac{4}{15} = \frac{x}{75}$

3. $\frac{x}{1.5} = \frac{5}{20}$

4. An English teacher needs to purchase 45 tickets to take her class to a play. Normally the tickets are $5.00 each. Because she is bringing students, she receives a 10% discount. How much money will she have left in her $225 budget?

5. Store A sells tarts at a rate of 6 dozen for $75. Store B sells them for $12 a dozen. Store C sells them for $26 for 2 dozen. Which store has the best price? Your work will justify your answer.

6. Match each to the appropriate unit of measure.

a. Area of the school parking lot	_____	square kilometers
b. Area of Canada	_____	square meters
c. Area of a nail head	_____	square centimeters
d. Area of a birthday card	_____	square millimeters

7. Ima Fowlup evaluated $8 - 2 \times 5 =$ and got 30. Can you help her find her mistake?

8. Translate this sentence into a number sentence. *Twice a number is less than 5 and the opposite of the number.*

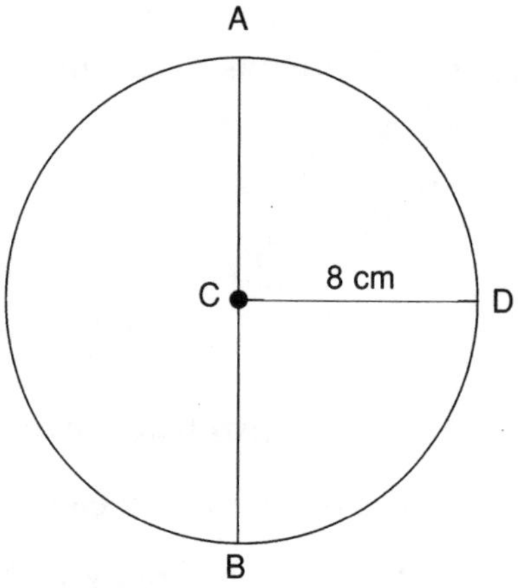

9. **Label the line segments: radius or diameter.**

 a. $\overline{AB}$ __________ $\overline{CD}$ __________

 b. Find the length of $\overline{AB}$.

10. a. **Draw the next two figures in the pattern.**

```
*    **    ***    ****
*    **    ***    ****
```

 b. How many dots are in the tenth figure? ________

11. **Compare using <, >, or =.**

 a. $|-4|$ __________ $|4|$ b. -4^2 __________ $(-4)^2$

 c. 2^4 __________ 4^2 d. $\frac{1}{3}$ __________ .3

12. **Let $x = -3$, let $y = -4$, and let $z = -5$. Find each of the following:**

 a. $x + y + z =$ b. $xyz =$

 c. $y^2 =$ d. $x + y \times z =$

1. Fill in the missing addends to make the sum correct.

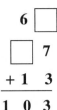

$$\begin{array}{r} 6\,\square \\ \square\,7 \\ +\,1\,3 \\ \hline 1\,0\,3 \end{array}$$

2. Estimate the quotient: $4986 \div 93 \approx$ ___________

3. Evaluate.

a. $8.14 \times 9.1 =$ b. $.078 \times .02 =$

4. Write the following sentence in algebraic notation. *Three more than twice a number is 15.*

5. What is the value of 7 in each number below?

a. 2.73 ___________ b. 1.467 ___________ c. 4.37 ___________

6. Terrance missed 8% of the questions on his test. The test had 50 questions. How many questions did he answer correctly?

7. A Boeing 737 jet airplane averages about 3 gallons of jet fuel per mile. How much fuel would be required to travel from New York City to London, England, a distance of 3471 miles.

8. Put + or – signs between these numbers to give the correct answer:

3 ☐ 4 ☐ 1 ☐ 5 ☐ 2 = 9

9. Evaluate and simplify.

a. $1\frac{1}{3} \div 2\frac{4}{9} =$

b. $6\frac{1}{8} \times \frac{1}{7} =$

10. Put in order from least to greatest:

$\frac{11}{12}$ $\frac{5}{6}$ $\frac{9}{10}$ $\frac{7}{8}$

__________ __________ __________ __________

11. At Miwauko's birthday party she served hot dogs and brownies. Each guest received the same number of hot dogs. Each also received the same number of brownies. Miwauko served 20 hot dogs and 30 brownies. What is the maximum number of guests at her party?

12. Add parentheses to make this sentence true.

$2 + 4 \times 3 - 2 + 3 = 19$

13. Ima Fowlup has a $2\frac{1}{2}$ pound bag of candy and wants to share $\frac{2}{3}$ of a pound with each of her three friends. She did the following math operation:

$$2\frac{1}{2} \div \frac{2}{3} = \frac{5}{2} \times \frac{3}{2} = \frac{15}{4} = 3\frac{3}{4}$$

"Wonderful," she exclaimed, "I have $\frac{3}{4}$ of a pound left for me". Explain her error and find how much she really has left over.

1. Lin counted the number of each color of *M & M's* in a 3–ounce package. She found the following: 6 brown, 5 red, 4 yellow, 3 green, 1 tan and 1 orange.
   a. Find the ratio of red to the total number. ______________
   b. If there were 100 *M & M's* in a 1-pound package, about how many would she expect to be red?

2. A recipe for a cake requires 1 teaspoon of vanilla. You have $1\frac{1}{2}$ ounces of vanilla. If a teaspoon is $\frac{1}{6}$ fluid ounce, how many cakes can you make?

3. A *polynomial* is an expression written as the sum or difference of terms. To simplify a polynomial, combine *like* terms. Simplify the following.
   a. $3a+4b-a$ b. $2x^2+x-x^2+3x^3$ c. $4x^2+9+x^2-5$

4. Mental math:
   a. $12 \div 10 =$ ______________ b. $12 \div 100 =$ ______________

5. Find two fractions that are equivalent to $\frac{3}{4}$: __________, __________

6. Figure ABCD is the *translation image* of figure WXYZ. (Think of a translation as moving or sliding a figure from one location to another. This may be a new concept for you.) Circle all of the following conclusions that are true.
   a. ABCD is congruent to WXYZ. b. $\angle A = \angle W$
   c. ABCD is a rectangle. d. BC = XY
   e. The area of ABCD = the area of WXYZ

7. Find the area of a triangle with $h = 4.3$ inches and $b = 2.5$ inches.

8. Write in exponential form.

a. $3 \times 3 \times 3$ ________

b. $\frac{1}{2} \times \frac{1}{2} \times \frac{1}{2} \times \frac{1}{2}$ ________

c. $a \times a \times a \times a \times a \times a$ ________

9. a. Find three pairs of numbers that satisfy the equation $y = \frac{1}{2}x$.

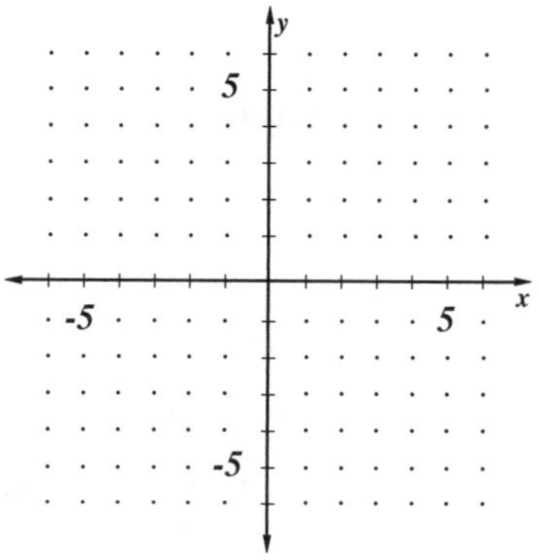

b. Plot these points on the graph at the right and draw a line through them.

c. Is the point (-2, 1) on the graph of your line?

10. Mental math: Your bill at the restaurant is $15. You want to leave a 20% tip. How much money will you leave?

a. $2.00 b. $3.00 c. $4.00 ________

11. 5 is what percent of 20?

1. By rearranging (*the commutative property*) or by regrouping (*the associative property*) you can often do math mentally. Use these properties to answer the following:

a. $80 + 33 + 20 =$ __________ b. $\frac{1}{3} \times \left(\frac{3}{4} \times 3\right) =$ __________

c. $62 + 47 + 38 =$ __________ d. $100 \times (8 \times .1) =$ __________

2. Evaluate and simplify.

a. $\begin{array}{r} 20\frac{2}{5} \\ -10\frac{9}{10} \\ \hline \end{array}$ b. $\begin{array}{r} 15\frac{1}{4} \\ -9\frac{3}{8} \\ \hline \end{array}$

3. Last year a class of 22 students paid \$33 for tickets to the museum. This year the cost for 22 students is \$44.

a. Find the unit price for each year.

b. By how much did they raise the price of one ticket?

4. $.14\overline{)2380}$

5. Find the least common multiple of 2, 4, and 6. ________

6. Using a 20% off discount card, you purchased a sweater for \$48.00. What was the original price of the sweater?

7. The sixth grade softball team has played 5 games and scored the following number of runs.

   2 15 5 4 6

   a. Find the mean.

   b. Find the median.

   c. Which do you think is the better measure of middle for this situation?

8. Only $\frac{2}{5}$ of the total set of dots have been drawn. * * *

   Draw the remaining dots to complete the set. * * *

9. Change this percent to a decimal, then to a fraction:

   $42\frac{1}{2}\ \% =$ ______________, ______________

10. Do the operations in the correct order to simplify: $4 + 2^2 - 9 \div (2+1) =$

11. Convert:

   a. 400 cm = ______________ m
   b. 500 ml = ______________ l
   c. 2 km = ______________ m
   d. 5 kg = ______________ g
   e. 10 cm = ______________ mm
   f. 500 g = ______________ kg

12. What figure am I?

   a. My opposite sides are equal.

   b. I have a right angle.

1. Mental math:

   a. $33\frac{1}{3}\%$ of 18 = __________ b. $66\frac{2}{3}\%$ of 18 = __________

2. How many times greater is the 9 in "a." than the 9 in "b."?

   a. 38,925,000,000 b. 38,829,000,000 __________

3. Mental math: A human being blinks an average of 1500 times in $2\frac{1}{2}$ hours.

   How many times will he blink in 10 hours?

4. a. $-5+(-7)=$ __________ b. $-5-(-7)=$ __________

5. A taxi ride costs $1.50 for the use of the cab and $.45 for each $\frac{1}{4}$ mile of travel. If you ride 4 miles, what is your "fare" (cost)?

6. Approximate where each of the following numbers would fall on the number line below. Mark the spots with the corresponding letters.

   a. $\frac{3}{4}$ b. $-2\frac{2}{3}$ c. $\sqrt{5}$ d. $-\frac{10}{3}$

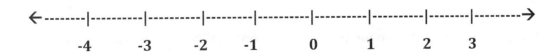

←--------|----------|----------|---------|----------|----------|----------|--------|---------→

-4 -3 -2 -1 0 1 2 3

7. Find the mean, median, and mode for the given number set.

   2 2 5 3 10 2 10 10 10

   a. mean ________ b. median ________ c. mode ________

   d. In this situation what do you think is the best measure of middle?

8. Simplify the following:

   a. $2a + 4b + c + 5a - 2b - c =$ ________ b. $3x + 5x^2 - 2x =$ ________

9. Let $a = 2$, $b = \frac{1}{2}$, $c = -2$, $d = -\frac{1}{2}$. Find the following:

   a. ab ________ b. ad ________ c. $a + b + c + d$ ________

   d. c^2 ________ e. d^2 ________ f. $\frac{ab}{cd}$ ________

10. Nancy has twice as many shells as Dee. Dee has three times as many shells as Jeannie. Jeannie has 17 shells.

    a. How many shells does Nancy have? ________

    b. How many shells does Dee have? ________

11. For problems a – c, solve for x. (Some will have more than one answer.)

    a. $x^2 = 9$ b. $\sqrt{x} = 5$ c. $|x| = 2$

For numbers 1 – 3, simplify:

1. $2a-(3b+2b)=$ 2. $2x^2y-xy^2=$ 3. $3(a+b)=$

4. A *rational number* is a number that can be written as a ratio of two integers (that is, as a fraction). Show that each number below is rational by renaming it as a fraction.

a. 2 b. $-.3$ c. $.\overline{3}$

d. 25% e. -10% f. .09

5. Solve for n.

a. $\frac{5}{8}=\frac{n}{40}$ b. $\frac{2}{3}=\frac{n}{24}$ c. $\frac{5}{6}=\frac{n}{27}$

6. Mental math: Estimate the sum by rounding to the nearest whole number.

$3.756+37.042\approx$

7. Which number is closest in value to 1.08?

a. 106% b. $1\frac{70}{1000}$ c. $\frac{103}{100}$ d. $\frac{110}{100}$

8. In many cities a realtor's commission is 5.5% of the selling price of a home. A certain home sold for $1,600,000. What was the realtor's commission on this sale?

9. Find the next number in this number sequence.

1, 2, 4, 7, 11, 16, 22, ________

10. A rectangle has two sides that are 6 feet, 11 inches and two that are 9 feet, 7 inches. What is the perimeter of this rectangle?

11. Deanine earned a 20% discount at Russel's Department Store. What will she pay for a pair of jeans originally priced at $38.00?

12. Translate each of the following into a number sentence.

a. $.10 times *n* cans returned is $5.50. ________________

b. Two times Henry's age, *a*, is less than than 8. ________________

c. Three times a number, *n*, is more than 20. ________________

13. Use <, >, or = to make each true.

a. $2 \times 6 \div 3$ ________ $6 \div 3 \times 2$

b. $\left(\frac{1}{2}\right)^3$ ________ $\left(\frac{1}{3}\right)^2$

c. $3 - (3 \div 3) \times 3$ ________ $(3 - 3) \div 3 \times 3$

d. 1.0^3 ________ $1{,}000{,}000^0$

For problems 1 and 2, evaluate and simplify.

1. $\frac{2}{3}+3\frac{1}{2}-\frac{5}{6}=$

2. $\frac{2}{3}\div\frac{2}{9}\times\frac{1}{4}=$

3. Round each number to the nearest tenth.

.86 ________ .75 ________ 1.98 ________ 3.209 ________

4. Use <, >, or == to make each sentence true.

a. 4^3 ________ 3^4

b. 200% ________ 2

c. -3^2 ________ $|-9|$

d. $\frac{1}{3}$ ________ 33%

5. Two rectangles are similar. The dimensions of the first are 2 feet × 8 feet. If the length of the second is 20 feet, what is its width?

6. A fair coin is tossed 10 times in a row. Each time it lands on heads. What is the probability that the coin will land on heads the 11th time it is tossed?

7. It took 140 chicken fingers to feed a class of 28 students. How many would you need to feed 70 students?

8. Evaluate and simplify.

a. $3\frac{3}{4}\times 6\frac{1}{2}=$

b. $1\frac{3}{4}\div\frac{1}{8}=$

9. What is 14 minus 0.356?

10. Translate each into an algebraic expression. Let n = number.

a. 4 more than half a number ______________

b. 2 less than a number ______________

c. The opposite of a number ______________

11. Solve for x. (Some may have more than one answer.)

a. $x^2 = 49$

b. $3^x = 27$

c. $|x| = 9$

12. Solve the following mentally by using the commutative property or the associative property.

a. $\$1.25+\$2.57+\$.75=$ __________

b. $-3+9+3+1=$ __________

c. $\left(\frac{2}{3}\times 5\right)\times\frac{3}{2}=$ __________

d. $\frac{1}{3}+\frac{4}{5}+\frac{2}{3}+\frac{1}{5}=$ __________

e. $4.8+1.9+1.2=$ __________

f. $-\frac{3}{5}\times 6\times\frac{5}{3}=$ __________

1. Distance, d, is rate, r, times time, t, or $d = rt$. How many miles per hour would you have to drive to get to a destination 520 miles away in 8 hours?

2. Mental math: Estimate these products.

   a. $28 \times 51 \approx$ ________ b. $103 \times 98 \approx$ ________

3. a. Give this measure in pounds and ounces: 86 ounces = ____________

   b. Give this measure in gallons and quarts: 30 pints = ____________

4. Mary Pat jogged for $\frac{5}{6}$ hour, Cindy for 45 minutes and Shanna for .6 hour. Who jogged the longest amount of time?

5. A certain store sells 2-liter bottles of pop for $1.19. They have a special on a 6-pack of 12 ounce cans for $1.50. (A 2-liter pop bottle contains approximately 67.2 ounces of beverage.)

   a. Find the unit price for each.

   b. Which is the better buy?

6. A commercial says, "A Widget sells for $20. If you buy now, we will discount your Widget 15%. But wait, if you buy in the next five minutes, we will give you a second Widget for free." You take advantage of this terrific deal.

   What will you pay per Widget?

7. Graph $|x| \le 3$ on the number line below.

←--------|----------|----------|----------|----------|----------|----------|----------|----------|--------→

-4 0 4

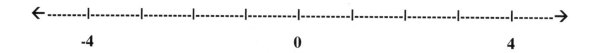

8. a. The volume, V, of a cube with side, s, is $V = s^3$. If a cube has volume, $V = 8$ cubic units, what is the length of each side?

   b. Suppose each side is tripled, what is the volume of the new cube?

9. Which of the following proportions are true?

   a. $\frac{2}{7} = \frac{10}{35}$ b. $\frac{2}{3} = \frac{18}{24}$ c. $\frac{4}{5} = \frac{48}{60}$

10. The *mean absolute deviation* (*MAD*) is an average of how far data values are from the mean value. (See "Help Pages," pg. 6) This may be a new concept for you.

    Follow the steps to find the MAD for the data points below.

    4 8 8 10 14 16

    (1) Find the mean. _______________

    (2) Find the deviation (absolute distance) of each point from the mean. $|mean - data\ value|$

    (3) $MAD = \dfrac{sum\ of\ deviations\ from\ mean}{number\ of\ data\ values}$ Find the *MAD* for this data set.

For problems 1-4, find the product and simplify.

1. $8 \times 1\frac{1}{2} =$
2. $2\frac{1}{4} \times 3\frac{1}{2} =$
3. $\frac{1}{2} \times \frac{3}{4} =$
4. $\frac{2}{3} \times \frac{5}{8} =$

5. Hair ribbon sells for $.58 per foot. Ima Fowlup needed 2.5 yards of ribbon. She found the cost by solving this proportion.

$$\frac{.58}{1} = \frac{x}{2.5}, \quad x = \$1.45$$

Explain and correct her mistake.

6. Maisie and Stitchie are two hungry kittens. You have exactly $\frac{3}{4}$ cup of milk. If you divide the amount equally, how much will each receive?

7. Mental math: Use the associative and commutative properties to solve the following.

a. $4 \times 2.25 \times 25 =$ ______________

b. $133 + 56 + 67 =$ ______________

c. $5 \times 3 \times 5 \times 2 =$ ______________

d. $7 + 1\frac{3}{5} + 3 + 7\frac{2}{5} =$ ______________

8. The scale on a set of house plans is: $\frac{1}{4}$ inch = 1 foot. How long is a wall on a room that measures $3\frac{1}{2}$ inches on the drawing?

9. Juan's father agreed to pay $\frac{1}{3}$ of the cost of Juan's new bike. Juan's father paid $37. How much did the bike cost?

10. If you began with $7.50 and spent $.25 on candy each day during the month of September, would you run out of money before the end of the month? (September has 30 days.)

11. Write "O" next to pairs of numbers that are opposites and "R" next to pairs of numbers that are reciprocals.

a. 3 and $\frac{1}{3}$ ________

b. .01 and 100 ________

c. 4 and -4 ________

d. $-\frac{2}{3}$ and $-\frac{3}{2}$ ________

12. Find the area of a circle with $r = 3$ inches. Round to the nearest tenth.

For problems 1-3, find the quotient and simplify.

1. $5 \div \frac{1}{5} =$

2. $2\frac{1}{2} \div 1\frac{2}{3} =$

3. $-\frac{3}{5} \div \frac{1}{10} =$

4. $7.3\overline{)1542}$

5. $.02\overline{).004}$

6. a. Draw and label a net for the prism pictured at the right. (See lesson 19, # 3 for an example of a net).

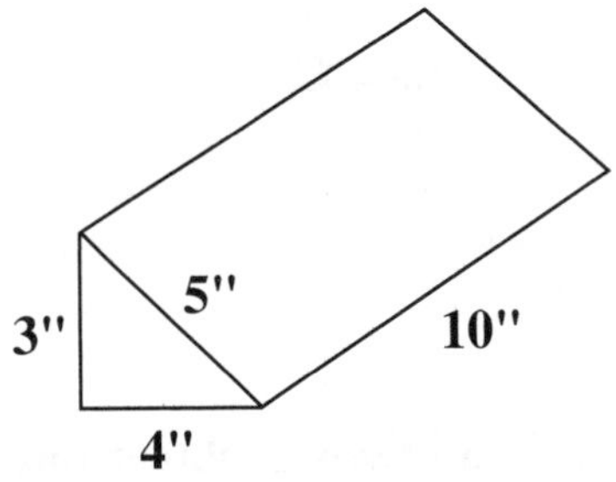

b. Find the surface area.

c. Find the volume.

7. The formula for the volume, V, of a sphere with radius, r, is $V = \frac{4}{3}\pi r^3$.

Use $\pi = 3.14$

a. Write the calculator sequence for finding the volume of a sphere with $r = 3$ inches.

b. Using your calculator, find the volume.

8. Calculate the numerical grade point averages for the following students. Use the scale below.

	Miles	Arianna	
4.0 = A	Math B	Math A	Miles: ________
3.7 = A-	English A-	English B	Arianna: ________
3.3 = B+	Science C	Science A-	
3.0 = B	History C+	History B	
2.7 = B-	Music B	Music C+	
2.3 = C+			
2.0 = C			

9. If a baseball player has a batting average of .250, how many hits would you predict him to have in 20 times at bat?

10. The "starting five" on the Lady Wildcats basketball team have the following heights:

65 in 66 in 66 in 68 in 70 in

a. Find the mean height, to the nearest inch. __________

b. Find the MAD.

c. Use a full sentence to explain the meaning of the MAD in this situation.

1. Find two numbers whose sum is 13 and whose product is 36.

2. Next year's sixth grade class is 15% larger than this year's class of graduating eighth graders. If 220 eighth graders are graduating, how big is the incoming sixth grade class?

3. Lizzie rode her bike 25 miles in 2.5 hours.
   a. Find her rate in miles per 1 hour.

   b. Find her rate in hours per 1 mile.

4. Mr. White posted the following box-and-whisker plot on his white board. He said that it represents the class's most recent scores on a math test. (The points represent the lowest score, the lower quartile, the median, the upper quartile, and the highest score.)

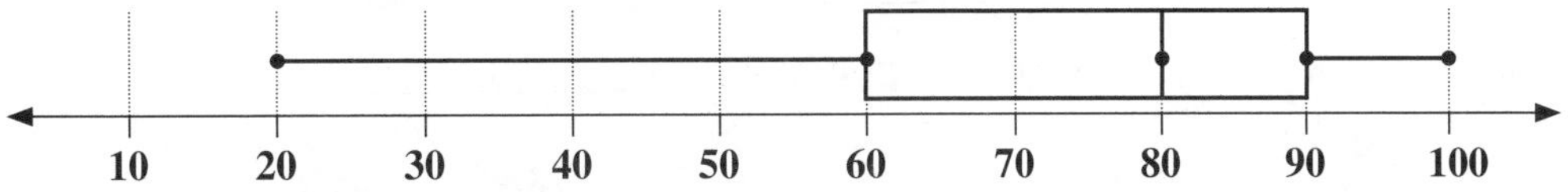

   a. What was the highest score? ___________
   b. What was the lowest score? ___________
   c. What was the median score? ___________
   d. What is the upper quartile? ___________
   e. What is the lower quartile? ___________
   f. What is the interquartile range? (upper quartile – lower quartile)
   ___________ (50% of the students are in this range.)
   g. Twenty eight students took the test. How many had a score of 90 or better? ___________

5. Find the greatest common factor of 81, 54, 36 ______________

6. Estimate the quotient to the nearest hundred. $5375 \div 6 \approx$ ______________

7. What number am I?

   a. I am an odd number

   b. I am divisible by 9.

   c. I am not divisible by 5.

   d. I am more than 20 and less than 50.

8. A kicker on a football team made 13 out of 17 field goal attempts. He made 25 out of 31 extra points attempts. Was he more likely to make a field goal or an extra point?

9. Estimate each of the following:

   a. The area of a square 4.1 units on a side __________

   b. The square root of 17 ______________

   c. The cost of 8 candy bars at $.99 per bar ______________

10. You just completed 30 lessons with an average of 11 problems per lesson.

    a. How many total problems have you worked?

    b. If each lesson took 30 minutes, what is your rate in problems per minute?

1. For problems, a – c simplify: (Recall that the order of operations is: parentheses, powers, multiplication and division from left to right; addition and subtraction from left to right.)

   a. $1 + 4^2 \times 3$ b. $16 - 4/2 + 3$ c. $100/25 - 2 \times 2$

2. Place the numbers 50%, 3^0, π, $\frac{4}{3}$, $-.75$, -2^2 on the number line below.

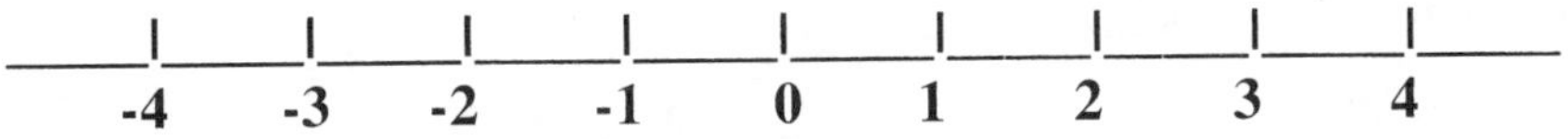

3. Place in order from least to greatest.
   1.91 1.09 1.119 1.19

4. Use <, > or = to make each sentence true.

   a. $3 \times 4 + 2$ __________ $3 + 4 \times 2$ b. $2 \times 2 - 1$ __________ $2 \times (2 - 1)$

   c. 1.0^3 __________ 10^0 d. $8 - (8 + 8)$ __________ $(8 - 8) + 8$

5. A *variable* is a symbol that can be replaced by a number.
   Let $a = -2$, $b = 3$, $c = 5$ Find each of the following:

   a. abc b. a^2 c. $c(a + b)$

6. Joe Smith hit 12 home runs in his first 15 games of the Triple-A baseball season. His team will play a total of 80 games. If this rate continues, how many home runs can Joe expect to hit?

7. a. Plot the following points on the coordinates to the right.
   $A = (-3, 1)$, $B = (4, 1)$, $C = (4, -2)$, $D = (-3, -2)$

   b. Connect the points in alphabetical order. Then connect D to A.

   c. Identify this figure.

   d. Find the area of this figure.

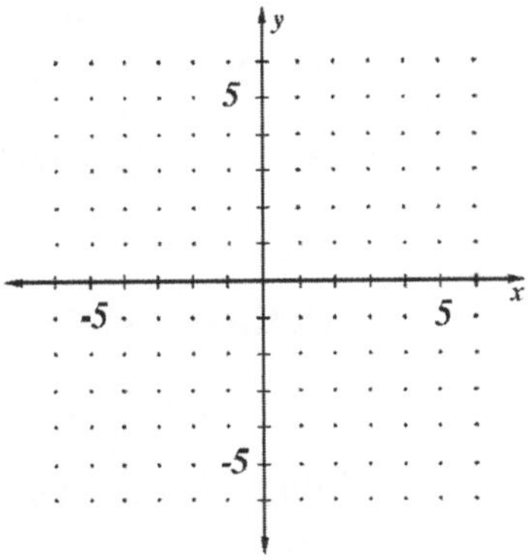

8. An *expression* occurs when numbers and variables are joined using arithmetic operations. Write each as an algebraic expression. Let n = the number.
   a. Five times a number ______________________
   b. Eight less than a number ______________________
   c. Three more than twice a number ______________________

9. An *arithmetic sequence* is a number pattern where the difference between consecutive numbers (terms) is constant.
   The first four terms of a sequence are 5, 13, 21, 29, …
   a. Find the next two terms in the sequence. ________, ________
   b. Find the difference between any two consecutive terms. (next term – previous term) ________
      This is the constant rate of change.
   c. State a rule to find any terms in this sequence.
   d. Use your rule to find the tenth term in this sequence. __________

10. Addison scored 40, 81, 86, 88, and 93 on her math tests. The mean and the median are measures of *central tendency.*
   a. Find the mean of her test scores.
   b. Find the median of her test scores.
   c. Eliminate the score of 40 and recalculate her mean and median. (The 40 is an *outlier.* An outlier is a score that varies widely from the rest of a data set.) Which measure was most affected by the score of 40?
   d. In this class the grading scale is:
      85-92 B   78 – 84 C
      What should Addison receive for her quarter grade?

1. For problems a – c, simplify:

   a. $6 \div 2 + 7 \times 3$ b. $8 + 40 / -5 - 3$ c. $\dfrac{8 + 40}{-5 - 3}$

2. Use <, >, or = to make each sentence true.

   a. $\frac{1}{2} + \frac{1}{2}$ ____ $\frac{1}{2} \times \frac{1}{2}$ b. $\frac{1}{2} \times \frac{1}{2}$ ____ $\frac{1}{2} \div \frac{1}{2}$

   c. $\frac{1}{2} \times \frac{1}{2}$ ____ $\frac{1}{2} \div 2$ d. $\left(\frac{1}{2}\right)^2$ ____ $\frac{1}{2} \times \frac{1}{2}$

3. A *number sentence* is formed when two expressions are related using a math verb. Some math verbs are $<, >, =, \leq, \geq, \neq, \cong$.
   Josiah has x dollars and Caleb has $22. Together they have more than $57.
   Write a number sentence to describe this situation.

4. Order the following from least to greatest: $\frac{3}{8}$ $\frac{1}{3}$ .35 .38

5. For problems a – c, solve for x.

   a. $2x = 6$ b. $\frac{1}{2}x = -10$ c. $\frac{1}{3}x + 3 = 5$

6. a. Identify two vertical angles. __________
   b. Identify two adjacent angles. __________

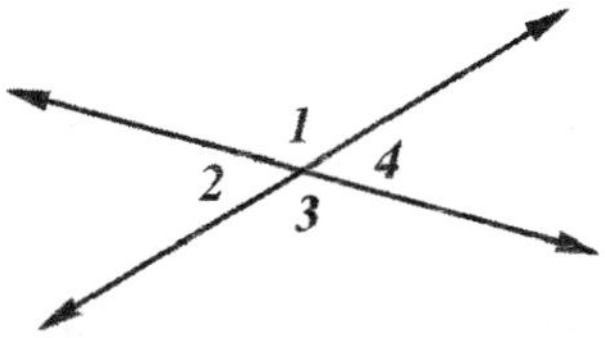

7. Suppose $a > 1$, $0 < b < 1$, $-1 < c < 0$, $d < -1$.

   a. Which is the largest?

   (1) b (2) $-a$ (3) c (4) $-d$

   b. Which is the smallest?

   (1) b (2) b^2 (3) $-b^2$ (4) $(-b)^2$

8. **a.** Find three pairs of numbers that satisfy the equation $x - y = 3$.

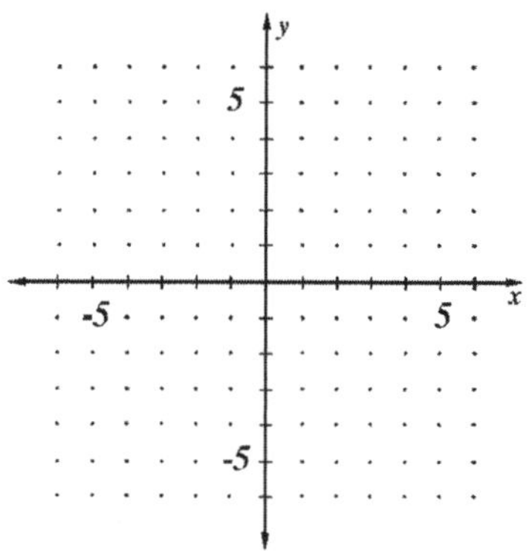

b. Plot the points on the graph at the right and connect them with a line.

c. Use your graph to find another ordered pair.

d. Substitute your point from c into $x - y = 3$ to show that it satisfies the equation.

9. An *equation* is a number sentence where the math verb is $=$.

Ben is 5 years older than Ann.

a. If Ann is a years old, write an expression for Ben's age. ____________

b. Ben is twice Ann's age. Write an equation to describe this.

c. Solve your equation, and find each age.

10. The *absolute value* of a number is its positive distance from zero. Find the absolute value of each of the following:

a. $|-3|$ **b.** $|3-10|$ **c.** $|15-2|$

11. Accurately draw a triangle congruent to ΔABC. Label it ΔDEF

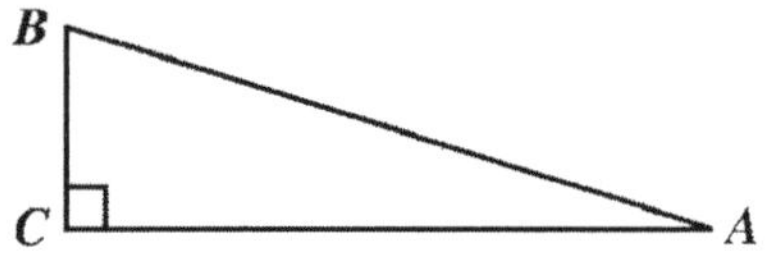

Lesson # 33

1. **Add parentheses to make the equation true.**

$$8 - 6 \times 16 \div 4 = 8$$

2. **Draw or construct the perpendicular bisector of $\overline{AB}$.**

3. **Some sixth graders want to estimate the population of turtles in a pond near their school. On a Friday they captured 10 turtles, marked their shells with a spot of nail polish, and released them back into the pond. One week later they recaptured 10 turtles. Four had the marking.**
   a. **Estimate the turtle population in the pond.**

   b. **What could the class do to get a more accurate estimation?**

4. **A *formula* is an equation stating that a single variable is equal to an expression. The circumference (c) of a circle with radius (r) is $c = 2\pi r$. Find the circumference of a circle with $r = 2\frac{1}{2}$ inches. Use $\pi \approx \frac{22}{7}$.**

5. **A six-sided die was tossed 100 times. The frequencies were recorded below.**

1	14 times	2	20 times	3	18 times
4	14 times	5	16 times	6	18 times

   a. **What was the frequency of the occurrence of 6? __________**
   b. **What is the probability of an outcome of 6 based on the data above?**
   __________ (This is the *experimental probability*.)
   c. **When a six-sided die is tossed, what is the expected probability of an outcome of 6? __________ (This is the *theoretical probability*.)**
   d. **Do you feel this was a fair die? Explain.**

6. a. Accurately draw ΔXYZ where $XY = 2''$, $m\angle X = 60°$ and $m\angle Y = 60°$.

   b. Find the $m\angle Z$.

   c. What kind of triangle is this? Justify your answer.

7. Let $x < 0$. Explain why $x^2 < 0$.

8. The area (A) of a parallelogram with base (b) and height (h) is $A = bh$.

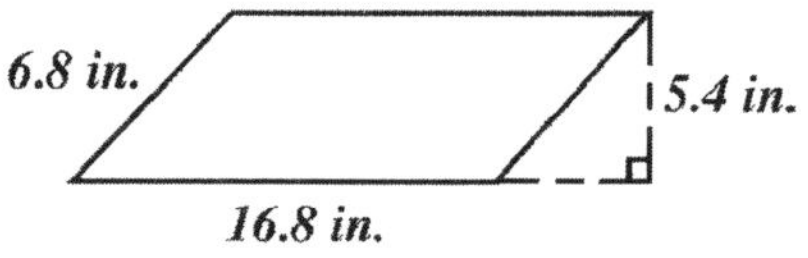

   a. Find the area of the parallelogram pictured at the right. Round your answer to the nearest tenth.

   b. What piece of information given in the picture is not necessary to answer question a?

9. Use the distribution property to find the missing number or variable.

   a. $3(x + y) = 3(\ \ ) + 3(\ \ )$ b. $(\ \ )(x + y) = 7x + 7y$

10. For problems a – c, solve for x.

   a. $2x + -4 = 12$ b. $29 - x = 15$ c. $\frac{2}{3}x = \frac{1}{2}$

11. Let $0 < x < 1$. Explain why $x^2 < x$.

1. Write each of the following in standard notation.

   a. 2.3×10^4 ______________

   b. 1.0×10^6 ______________

2. Use the triangle pictured at the right. Find the measure of each angle.

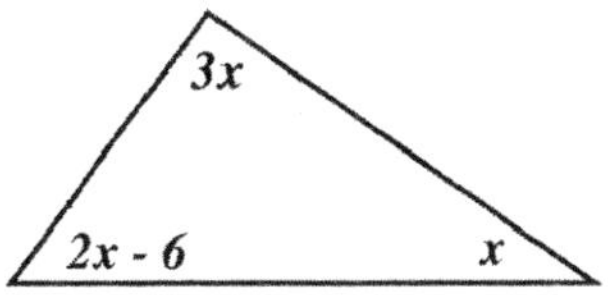

3. The mean, median, and mode are measures of *central tendency*. Find the mean, median, and mode for the following number set.

   4 8 9 2 7 8 8 3 4 1

   a. mean __________ b. median __________ c. mode __________

4. The area (A) of a circle with radius (r) is $A = \pi r^2$.

   a. Find the area of a circle with $r = 3$ inches. Use $\pi \approx 3.14$.

   b. Will the answer be an exact or an approximate answer? Explain.

5. Choose from the associative property, commutative property, or distributive property to justify each of the following:

   a. $3(2 + x) = 6 + 3x$ ________________________

   b. $3 \times 25 \times 4 = 4 \times 25 \times 3 = 300$ ________________________

   c. $(8 + 22) + -8 = (8 + -8) + 22 = 22$ ________________________

6. If two angles are *supplementary*, then their sum is 180°.

   a. Write an algebraic sentence (equation) to describe the situation pictured at the right.

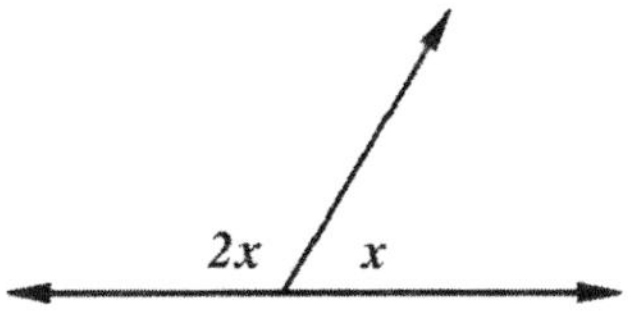

   b. Solve for x.

7. Find the measure of each angle pictured at the right.

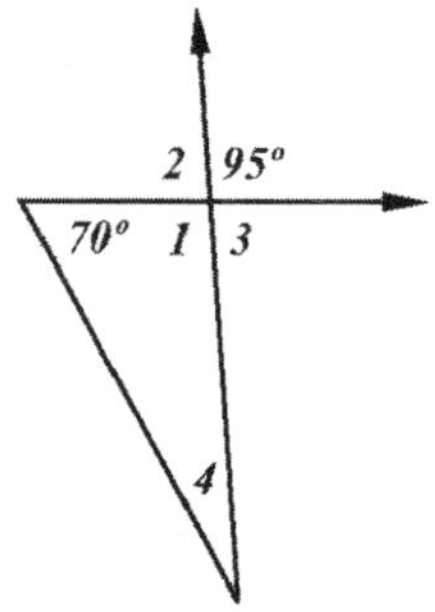

a. $m\angle 1$ __________ b. $m\angle 2$ __________

c. $m\angle 3$ __________ d. $m\angle 4$ __________

8. A standard deck of cards contains 52 cards. There are 13 spades, 13 hearts, 13 diamonds, and 13 clubs. There are three face cards in each suit: jacks, queens, and kings. Find the probability of each.

a. P(10) __________ b. P(jack or queen) __________

c. P(two aces) __________

9. If two angles are *complementary*, then their sum is 90°.

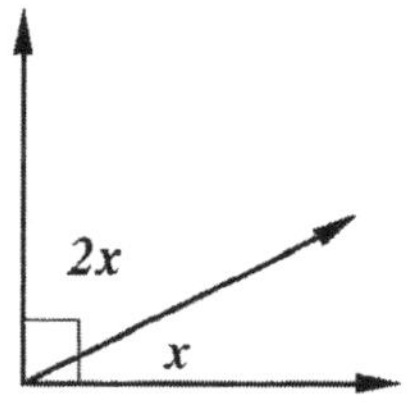

a. Write algebraic sentence (equation) to describe the situation pictured at the right.

b. Find the measure of each angle.

10. A biased sample is one in which members of a population are underrepresented or ignored totally.

The student council wanted to select an activity for Friday's after-school party. They randomly asked 25 students from the after-school sports practices to select an activity. The next day the council announced that the students chose to have a three-on-three basketball tournament.

Explain why their sample may be biased.

1. A random sample of a population needs to satisfy two criteria:
   A) Each member of the population needs to have an equal likelihood of being selected.
   B) Each member is chosen independently of any other member.

   The school cafeteria wishes to select a sample of 30 students to recommend menu items for school lunches. Determine whether or not each group below is a representative sample. Justify your response.

   a. The thirty members of the wrestling squad.

   b. The first thirty students to volunteer to be in the group.

   c. Thirty students computer selected from all school attendance sheets.

2. Elaine baby-sits for $8.50 per hour.
   a. Complete the table to show her wage (w) per hour (h) worked.

$h =$	0	1	2	3	4	5	6
$w =$							

   b. Write an equation for her wage in terms of hours.
   c. Plot the points on the coordinates at the right.
   d. Should these points be connected to form a line? Explain your reasoning.

   e. If Elaine baby-sits for 10 hours, how much can she expect to earn?

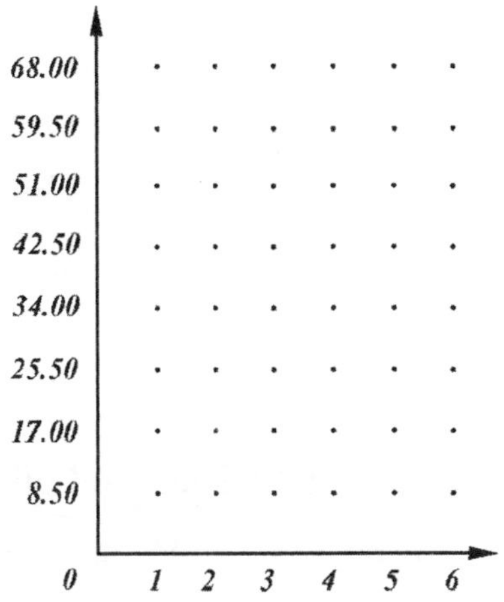

3. In the sequence $3\frac{1}{2}$, $2\frac{3}{4}$, 2,.....

   a. Find the next two terms in the sequence. __________, __________

   b. Find the constant rate of change. __________

   c. Find a rule for any term in this sequence.

   d. Use your rule to find the tenth term in this sequence. __________

4. $m\angle 1 = 130°$. Find the measures of the other angles. Justify each response.

	Measure	Justification
a. $m\angle 2$		
b. $m\angle 3$		
c. $m\angle 4$		

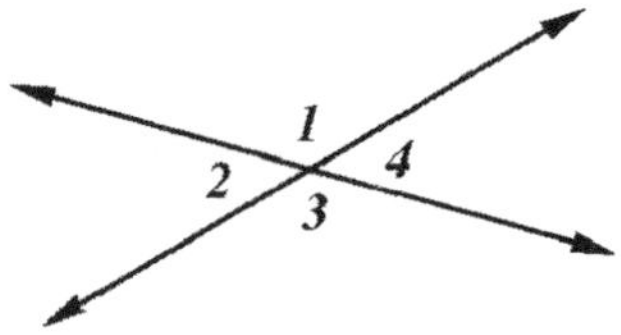

5. Accurately draw a parallelogram with $b = 3$ inches and $h = 1.5$ inches.

6. a. Rewrite $4 \times .04 + 4 \times .06$ using the distributive property.

   b. Evaluate.

7. Your best friend multiplied $.034 \times 5.3$ and answered 1.802. His decimal point is misplaced. Explain to him how to accurately determine decimal placement.

6th Grade

BRAIN AEROBICS - WEEK 1

1. If it is 12:00 P.M. and you move the minute hand 90 degrees clockwise, what time will it be?

2. Mandy could not decide which was the better bargain for juice boxes for her kindergarten class; 45 boxes for $10.80, or 15 boxes for $3.75?

3. Andrea's family loves to eat turkey at Thanksgiving. She plans on $1\frac{1}{4}$ pounds for each adult in the family and $\frac{3}{4}$ pound for each child. Andrea expects 14 children and 10 adults. Will a 22 pound turkey be enough to feed her guests?

4. Cheryl drove 125 miles from Ann Arbor, Michigan to Grand Rapids, Michigan. How many miles did she drive if she made two round trips?

5. Arrange these numbers in the boxes below to give the largest possible answer in this subtraction problem. Use each number only once. (7, 9, 3, 4, 0, 1)

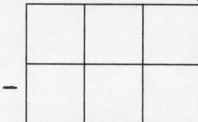

−			

Solutions – Brain Aerobics – Week 1 – 6th Grade

1.

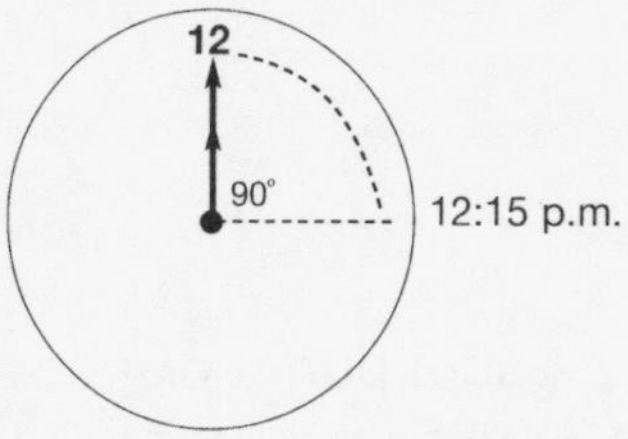

2. 10.80 ÷ 45 = .24
3.75 ÷ 15 = .25
45 boxes for $10.80 is the better buy

3. 1.25 x 10 = 12.5 pounds for adults
.75 x 14 = 10.5 pounds for children
12.5 + 10.5 = 23 pounds needed therefore the 22 pound turkey will not be enough.

4. 125 x 2 = 250 miles for one round trip
250 x 2 = 500 miles for two round trips

5.

	9	7	4
–	0	1	3

BRAIN AEROBICS - WEEK 2

1. Richard starts high school every day at 7:45 A.M. How many seconds is Richard in school each day if school dismisses at 2:15 P.M.?

2. Sondra bought shoes that had a .25 foot heel. If she is 6 feet tall with these shoes on, how tall is she without her shoes?

3. Jamie ate three pieces of candy. Bill ate twice as much as Jamie. Tom ate twice as much as Bill. How many total pieces did the three boys eat?

4. In Minot, North Dakota, the temperature was 15 degrees Fahrenheit at 4:00 P.M. By 11:00 P.M. the temperature had fallen 17 degrees. What was the temperature at 11:00 P.M.?

5. Kristen found that in 8th grade she studies 2.2 hours a week more than she did in 7th grade. If this trend continues until her senior year of high school, how many more hours will she study per week in 12th grade than she did in 7th grade?

Solutions – Brain Aerobics – Week 2 – 6th Grade

1. 7:45 to 2:15 is 6.5 hours
6.5 x 60 = 390 minutes
390 x 60 = 23,400 seconds

2. .25 x 12 = 3 inches
6'0" - 3" = 5'9" (' means feet, " means inches)

3. x = amount of candy Jamie ate
2 x = amount of candy Bill ate
4 x = amount of candy Tom ate
x = 3, so 3 + (2 • 3) + (4 • 3) = 21 pieces in all

4. 15 - 17 = -2° F

5. Grade 7 \ 2.2 / 8 \ 2.2 / 9 \ 2.2 / 10 \ 2.2 / 11 \ 2.2 / 12
2.2 x 5 = 11 hours

BRAIN AEROBICS - WEEK 3

1. If it is 3:00 P.M. and you move the minute hand of the clock 270 degrees clockwise, what time will it be?

2. Lenora wants to buy granola bars for her hiking trip. Eight bars cost $2.40. She wants to buy 12 bars. How much will 12 bars cost?

3. Aaron stood in line to ride the Millennium Force roller coaster. After Aaron stood in line for $\frac{1}{2}$ hour, he realized that he waited only $\frac{1}{4}$ of the total time he had to wait in line. How long will he have to wait in line?

4. Mrs. Bergman has 7 gallons of gasoline in her car. Her car travels 25 miles for each gallon of gas burned. She needs to go to Boston which is 400 miles away. How many gallons of gas does she need to put in her car so that she still has 2 gallons left when she reaches Boston?

5. Ralph's t-shirt shop is having a once-a-year sale. If you buy one t-shirt, you receive the second one for 20% off, the third one for 25% off, and so on. How many t-shirts would you have to buy to receive a free shirt?

Solutions – Brain Aerobics – Week 3 – 6th Grade

1.

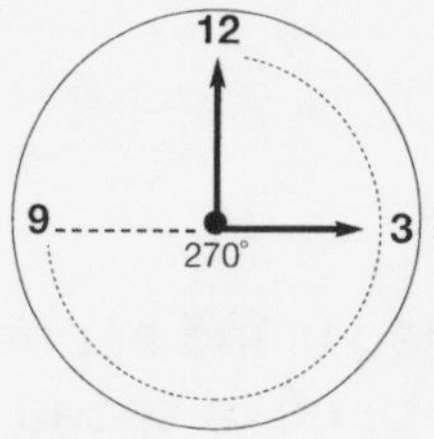

3:45 p.m.

2. 2.40 ÷ 8 = .30 per bar
.30 x 12 = $3.60

3. $\frac{1}{2}$ hour = .5 hour
.5 x 4 = 2 hours

4. 400 ÷ 25 = 16 gallons to drive to Boston
16 + 2 = 18 gallons needed
She already has 7, so 18 - 7 = 11 gallons must be added

5.

%	%	%	%	
2 - 20	6 - 40	10 - 60	14 - 80	
3 - 25	7 - 45	11 - 65	15 - 85	18th shirt is free.
4 - 30	8 - 50	12 - 70	16 - 90	
5 - 35	9 - 55	13 - 75	17 - 95	

BRAIN AEROBICS - WEEK 4

1. Tony saw 11 riders and 26 wheels. How many bicycles did he see? How many tricycles?

2. Jock was studying the author Mark Twain in his literature class. The first week he read 10% of the 550 pages in Tom Sawyer plus $\frac{1}{4}$ of the 420 pages in Huckleberry Finn. How many pages did he read in all?

3. Tamara's softball team is in a league with 3 other teams. Each season, every team plays the other 3 teams 4 times each. How many season games does each team play in all?

4. When you add the numbers in this 3 digit palindrome together, the sum is 4. What is the number? (Hint: There are two possible answers.)

5. The Coaches' Association membership dues are $500 per year. Members are given a $50 per year reduction in their dues for every 5 years they've been a member. Nancy has been a member for 20 years. How much does she pay in dues?

Solutions – Brain Aerobics – Week 4 – 6th Grade

1. 7 • 2 = 14 wheels on 7 bicycles
26 - 14 = 12
12 ÷ 3 = 4 tricycles

7 bicycles and 4 tricycles

2. .10 x 550 = 55 pages
.25 x 420 = 105 pages
55 + 105 = 160 pages

3. Each team plays 12 games.

4. 121 or 202

5. 20 ÷ 5 = 4
4 x 50 = $200 deduction
500 - 200 = $300 in dues

BRAIN AEROBICS - WEEK 5

1. If a baby was born on January 2, 1999, how old would he be on January 1, 2000?

2. Reuben drank one pint of milk for breakfast, $\frac{1}{2}$ quart of milk for lunch, and $\frac{1}{8}$ gallon of milk for dinner. How many pints of milk did he drink in all?

3. It took Hank 8 hours in total to build his model airplane. His cousin, Dan, took $3\frac{1}{2}$ times as long to build his. How many hours did Dan work on his model airplane?

4. This number is greater than 200 and less than 300. It is divisible by 9 and 7. What is the number?

5. The National Weather Service predicts a 60% chance of rain with a 20% chance that the rain will change to snow. What is the percent chance that there will be no precipitation?

Solutions – Brain Aerobics – Week 5 – 6th Grade

1. 1 day short of 1 year

2. 2 pints = 1 quart so $\frac{1}{2}$ quart = 1 pint
8 pints = 1 gallon so $\frac{1}{8}$ gallon = 1 pint
1 + 1 + 1 = 3 pints

3. 8 x 3.5 = 28 hours

4. 252

5. 100 % - 60% = 40% chance of no precipitation
(You do not need to use the 20% to solve this problem.)

BRAIN AEROBICS - WEEK 6

1. Stan earned $225 for 30 hours of work. Matt earned $290 for 40 hours of work. Who earned the most money per hour?

2. Andrea left for the park at 11:35 A.M. She returned 150 minutes later, took a $\frac{1}{2}$ hour nap, then walked 10 minutes to her friend's house. At what time did Andrea arrive at her friend's house?

3. Celeste is 5 years old. Her mother is 30. The ratio of Celeste's age to her mother's age is $\frac{5}{30}$ or $\frac{1}{6}$. What will the ratio be in 10 years? In 20 years?

4. Two cars are traveling in opposite directions at 70 miles per hour. How far apart will they be in 5 hours?

5. The election polls showed that a candidate had 54% of the vote. His opponent had 43% of the vote, and the rest of the voters were undecided. What percent of the voters were undecided?

Solutions – Brain Aerobics – Week 6 – 6th Grade

1. 225 ÷ 30 = 7.50/hour   Stan
290 ÷ 40 = 7.25/hour   Matt
Stan earned more money per hour.

2. 150 ÷ 60 = 2.5 hours
2.5 + .5 = 3 hours
3 hrs. 10 minutes until she arrived at her friend's house.
2:45 p.m.

3. $\frac{5 + 10 = 15}{30 + 10 = 40} = \frac{3}{8}$

$\frac{5 + 20 = 25}{30 + 20 = 50} = \frac{1}{2}$

4. 70 x 5 = 350 miles
350 x 2 = 700 miles apart

5. 54 + 43 = 97%
100 - 97 = 3% undecided

BRAIN AEROBICS - WEEK 7

1. Halley's comet is seen from Earth every 76 years. It was first seen in 1682 by Edmund Halley, an English astronomer. Name the next year we will be able to see Halley's comet.

2. Sabrina is baking cookies to sell for a student council fund raiser. Her recipe makes four dozen cookies. The ingredients are as follows:

2 cups flour	2 cups chocolate chips
2 eggs	1 cup chopped nuts
1 cup brown sugar	1 teaspoon vanilla
1/2 teaspoon baking soda	1 cup granulated sugar
1 cup butter	1/4 teaspoon salt

Change Sabrina's recipe so it will make 960 cookies.

3. Cynthia multiplied a number by four instead of dividing it by four. Her incorrect answer was 64. What should her answer have been?

4. The scale on a map showed that each inch represented 500 actual miles. Denise wanted to know the approximate distance between 2 cities that measured $3\frac{1}{4}$ inches apart on the map. What was the approximate distance between the two cities?

5. Using these 3 digits (3, 8, 6), make as many 3 digit numbers as possible. Use each digit only once in each number.

Solutions – Brain Aerobics – Week 7 – 6th Grade

1. 1682 + 76 = 1758
1758 + 76 = 1834
1834 + 76 = 1910
1910 + 76 = 1986
1986 + 76 = 2062

2. 960 ÷ 48 = 20 batches of cookies needed

2 x 20 = 40 cups flour	2 x 20 = 40 cups choc. chips
2 x 20 = 40 eggs	1 x 20 = 20 cups nuts
1 x 20 = 20 cups brown sugar	1 x 20 = 20 tsp. vanilla
$\frac{1}{2}$ x 20 = 10 tsp. b. soda	1 x 20 = 20 cups granulated sugar
1 x 20 = 20 cups butter	$\frac{1}{4}$ x 20 = 5 tsp. salt

3. 64 ÷ 4 = 16
16 ÷ 4 = 4
Her answer should have been 4.

4. 3.25 x 500 = 1625 miles

5. 386
368
836
863
638
683

BRAIN AEROBICS - WEEK 8

1. George is seven years older than John and two years older than Ricardo. The total of their ages is 48 years. How old is each person?

2. One half of the guest that attended Jenelle's birthday party left before 10:00 P.M. One fourth of the original number guests left at 11:00 P.M. After 11:00 P.M., 30 guests remained. How many people attended the party?

3. What are these 2 mystery numbers on the number line? One of the numbers is negative and the other is positive. The 2 numbers are 7 spaces apart on the number line. One number is 6 times closer to 0 than the other number. What are the two numbers? Draw a number line to assist you. (Hint: There are two possible answers.)

4. Using the year 2000, write the fraction that shows the comparison of your birthday (1 day) to the total number of days in the year. Do the same for the year 2001. (Hint: Remember the year 2000 was a leap year.)

5. A poll predicted that 65% of the voters were in favor of a school millage. This poll had a 3% margin of error. What would be the lowest and highest percentages of the voters voting in favor of the school millage?

Solutions – Brain Aerobics – Week 8 – 6th Grade

1. George = x years old
John = x - 7 years old
Ricardo = x - 2 years old

x + (x - 7) + (x - 2) = 48
3 x -9 = 48
3 x = 57
x = 19 George
x - 7 = 12 John
x - 2 = 17 Ricardo

2. 30 = $\frac{1}{4}$ of the guests
30 x 4 = 120 guests total

3. 

or 

4. For the year 2000, $\frac{1}{366}$ For the year 2001, $\frac{1}{365}$

5. 65 + 3 = 68%
65 - 3 = 62%

BRAIN AEROBICS - WEEK 9

1. What number am I? I have 3 digits. My first digit is twice the size of my second digit. My second digit is twice the size of my third digit. If you add my digits together, the sum is 14.

2. Jason arrived at Courtney's house 10 minutes after Terrence. Terrence arrived 5 minutes before Alina. Alina arrived at Courtney's house at 7:15 P.M. At what time did Jason arrive? At what time did Terrence arrive?

3. Kelly's first job out of college paid $40,000 dollars per year. She planned to save $\frac{1}{10}$ of her salary each year. The second year she made $42,000 and the third year $45,000. How much will she save during these first three years?

4. A series of 5 tests is required in Chad's history class. He needs to earn a 94% average to receive an A in the class. The scores on his first four tests were 98%, 98%, 100%, and 90%. What is the minimum score he needs on the fifth test to maintain a 94% average?

5. A book publishing company sold 30,000 books one year. The next year it increased its sales by 100%. How many books did the company sell the next year?

Solutions – Brain Aerobics – Week 9 – 6th Grade

1. 842

2. 7:15 - :05 = 7:10 Terrence
7:10 + :10 = 7:20 Jason

3. 40,000 x .10 = 4,000
42,000 x .10 = 4,200
45,000 x .10 = 4,500
4,000 + 4,200 + 4,500 = $12,700

4. 98
98
100
90
x

$$\frac{98 + 98 + 100 + 90 + x}{5} \geq 94$$

$$\frac{386 + x}{5} \geq 94$$

$$386 + x \geq 470$$

$$x \geq 84\%$$

5. 30,000 is 100% of 30,000
30,000 + 30,000 = 60,000 books

BRAIN AEROBICS - WEEK 10

1. Members of the cleaning crew were paid according to how long they had been working for the company. James and Gregorio were paid $14.25 per hour. Francine, Jamal, and Chris were paid $12.75 per hour. If the crew worked a 40 hour work week, how much would the company pay its five employees in total?

2. Max rode his bike 30 mph for the first hour, 27 mph for the next two hours, and 24 mph for the last hour. What was his average speed for the four hour bike ride?

3. Mrs. Brink found a carpet cleaner who cleans carpet for $.15 a square foot. Her family room measures 20 feet by 15 feet. How much will she pay to have her carpet cleaned?

4. Angie walks $\frac{1}{3}$ mile to school and $\frac{1}{3}$ mile home each day. If she gets a ride each way to school half the time, how many miles does she walk to and from school each school year? (Hint: A school year is 180 days.)

5. Desmond ran a lemonade stand in front of his house for the fans walking to the football game. On the first Saturday he sold 80 cups of lemonade. The second Saturday was cold and rainy so he sold only 70% of what he had sold the previous Saturday. How many cups did he sell on the second Saturday?

Solutions – Brain Aerobics – Week 10 – 6th Grade

1. 14.25 x 40 = 570.00 x 2 = 1,140
12.75 x 40 = 510.00 x 3 = +1,530
$ 2,670 Total

2. 30 + 27 + 27 + 24 = 108
108 ÷ 4 = 27 mph

3. 20 x 15 = 300 sq. ft. family room
300 x .15 = $45.00

4. $\frac{1}{3} + \frac{1}{3} = \frac{2}{3}$ mile each day she walks
180 ÷ 2 = 90 days she walks
$90 \times \frac{2}{3} = \frac{180}{3} = 60$ miles

5. 80 x .70 = 56 cups of lemonade

The Metric Units

Temperature - Celsius
0°C: the freezing point of water
37°C: the normal body temperature
100°C: the boiling point of water

Mass
1000 milligrams (mg) = 1 gram
1000 grams = 1 kilogram (kg)
1000 kilograms = 1 metric ton (t)

Capacity
1000 milliliters (mL) = 1 liter (L)
1000 liters = 1 kiloliter (kL)

Length
10 millimeters (mm) = 1 centimeter
10 centimeters (cm) = 1 decimeter
1000 millimeters (mm) = 1 meter (m)
100 centimeters = 1 meter (m)
10 decimeters (dm) = 1 meter
1000 meters (m) = 1 kilometer (km)

The Customary Units

Temperature - Fahrenheit
32°F: the freezing point of water
98.6°F: the normal body temperature
212°F: the boiling point of water

Weight
1 pound (lb) = 16 ounces (oz)
1 ton = 2,000 pounds

Time
1 minute (min) = 60 seconds (s)
1 hour = 60 minutes
1 day = 24 hours
1 week = 7 days
1 month (mo) = approx. 4 weeks
1 year (yr) = 365 days
52 weeks
12 months
1 decade = 10 years
1 century = 100 years

Capacity
1 cup (c) = 8 fluid ounces (fl oz)
1 pint (pt) = 16 fluid ounces
2 cups
1 quart (qt) = 32 fluid ounces
4 cups
2 pints
1 gallon (gal)= 128 fluid ounces
16 cups
8 pints
4 quarts

Length
1 foot (ft) = 12 inches (in)
1 yard (yd) = 36 inches
3 feet
1 mile (mi) = 5,280 feet
1,760 yards

GLOSSARY OF TERMS AND FORMULAS

a.m.: a way of expressing time between 12:00 midnight and 12:00 noon.

absolute value: the positive distance from zero.

acute angle: an angle measuring less than 90 degrees.

addends: numbers to be added together in an addition problem.

algebraic expression: a combination of numbers and variables joined by the operations of arithmetic.

angle: the union of two rays (the sides) at a point (the vertex).

area: the number of square units or parts of square units required to cover a two-dimensional figure.

Formula examples: parallelogram: $A = hb$ trapezoid: $A = \frac{1}{2} h(b_1 + b_2)$

triangle: $A = \frac{1}{2} hb$ rectangle: $A = lw$

circle: $A = \pi r^2$ square: $A = s^2$

arithmetic sequence: a number pattern where the difference between consecutive numbers (terms) is constant.

average: a number obtained by adding a group of numbers together and dividing by the number of addends.

biased sample: one in which members of a sample are underrepresented or totally ignored.

center: the point from which all points on a circle are equally distant.

circle: the set of all points equally distanct (the radius) from a point (the center).

circumference: the distance around a circle.

Formula: $c = 2\pi r$ where r = radius $\pi \approx 3.14$

common denominator: a multiple of all denominators in a problem.

common factor: a number that is a factor of two other numbers is a common factor.

Example: 3 is a common factor of 9 and 12.

common multiple: a number that is a multiple of two other numbers.

Example: 24 is a common multiple of 6 and 4.

complementary angles: two angles with a sum of 90 degrees.

congruent: refers to figures that have the same shape and size.

congruent figure: the image of another figure under a translation, reflection or rotation.

coordinates: number pairs used in graphing. The horizontal axis is listed first and the vertical axis is listed second.

Example: 8, 10

customary measurement: units of measurement used in the United States.
Example: feet, pounds, miles, etc.

cylinder: a solid object with two identical circular ends (think of a soup can).

decade: a period of 10 years.

decimal point: a period put just before the decimal fraction such as the periods in .625 and .08.

degree: a unit used to measure an angle or temperature.

degrees Celsius (C°): metric unit of measurement for temperature.

degrees Fahrenheit (F°): customary unit of measurement for temperature.

denominator: number below the line in a fraction.
Example: $\frac{1}{2}$ ⇐denominator

diameter: a segment connecting two points on a circle that contains the center.

difference: the answer to a subtraction problem.

digits: symbols used to write numbers.
Example: 6, 7, 8, etc.

divisor: a number by which another number is to be divided. When you divide the number 6 by 2, 2 is the divisor.

equal: when two or more numbers or items are the same in value, size or number.

equation: occurs when two expressions are joined by an = sign.

estimate: to find an answer that is close to the exact answer.

even number: a number that has 0, 2, 4, 6, or 8 in the one's place.

expanded form: a way to write numbers to show the place value of each digit.
Example: 1,322 = 1,000 + 300 + 20 + 2

exponent: is a number that shows how many times a base is used as a factor.
Ex. $x^3 = x \times x \times x$

factor: any one of the numbers that when multiplied gives a product.
Example: 4 x 5 = 20

fraction: a number that represents part of a set or region.

formula: an equation that states that a single variable is equal to an expression made up of one or more different variables.

function: a relationship where each member of the domain is paired with exactly one member of the range.

greater than (>): a way to show that one number is larger than another.
Example: 9 > 2 means "9 is greater than 2."

greatest common factor: the largest number that can be a factor of each of two other numbers.

hypotenuse: the side opposite the right angle in a right triangle.

integer: any whole number and its opposite.

interest: a fee paid for the privilege of borrowing money.

intersecting: the point or points that are the same for two sets of points or elements.

Example: 

inverse operation: the "opposite" operation.

Example: addition is the inverse of subtraction.

irrational numbers: a number that cannot be written as a quotient (fraction).

Example: π, $\sqrt{2}$

least common denominator (LCD): the lowest common multiple of two or more denominators.

least common multiple (LCM): the lowest number (not a zero) that is a multiple of two given numbers.

less than ($<$): a way to show one number is smaller than another.

Example: $2 < 9$ means "2 is less than 9."

line: a series of points that extends in opposite directions without end.

line segment: a part of a line that has two endpoints.

lowest terms: a fraction when the numerator and denominator have no common factor larger than 1.

mean: the average of a data set.

median: the middle number in a set of numbers when that set is arranged in order. When there is not a middle number, the median is the average of the two middle numbers.

mental math: performing calculations in a person's head without pencil or paper.

metrics: unit of measurement.

Example: centimeters, kilograms, milliliters

mixed number: a combination of a whole number and a fraction.

Example: $3\frac{1}{2}$

multiple: the product of a number and any non-zero number.

negative number: a number that is less than zero.

number line: a line that shows where numbers fall in order.

Example: 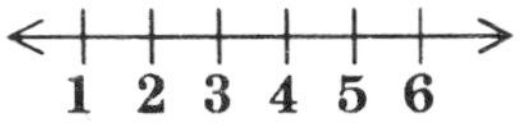

number sentence: occurs when two expressions are joined by a math verb.

Examples of math verbs are $=, \leq, \geq, <$, and $>$.

numerator: the number above the line in a fraction.

Example: $\frac{5}{8}$ ⇐numerator

numeral: number

numerical expression: an expression that contains two or more numbers.

Example: 6 + 2

obtuse angle: an angle measuring more than 90 degrees.

odd number: a whole number containing 1, 3, 5, 7, or 9 in the one's place.

opposites: two numbers that are the same distance from zero on the number line. The sum of opposites is zero.

Example: -1 + 1 = 0

outlier: a number that varies widely from the rest of a data set.

p.m.: a way of expressing time from 12:00 noon to 12:00 midnight.

parallel: two lines in the same plane that do not intersect or are the same.

Example: 

parallelogram: a quadrilateral with opposite sides parallel.

Example:  or 

percent: %, times $\frac{1}{100}$, per 100.

perfect square: the square of an integer.

Example: since $2^2 = 4$, 4 is a perfect square.

perimeter: the distance around a figure (the sum of all its sides).

perpendicular lines: two lines that intersect (cross) and form right angles (90° angles).

Example: 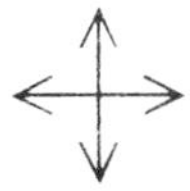

place value: the value given to the place a digit occupies in a number.

Example: 427 (4 is in the hundreds place, 2 is in the tens place and 7 is in the ones place.)

polygon: a figure formed by three or more line segments, each of which intersects exactly two others at their endpoints, to make a closed figure.

polynomial: an expression containing one or more terms.

positive number: a number that is more than zero.

profit: money received from a business venture after all expenses have been paid.

predict: to guess what will happen.

prime number: a number greater than 1 that can only be divided evenly by itself and the number 1.

prism: a three-dimensional figure with rectangular or parallelogram sides and parallel, congruent bases.

probability: is the number of favorable outcomes divided by the number of possible outcomes, when all outcomes are equally likely to occur.

product: the answer to a multiplication problem.

proportion: equal rates or ratios.

pyramid: a three-dimensional figure with triangular sides that meet at a vertex and a base that is a polygon.

Pythagorean theorem: in a right triangle, the square of the hypotenuse is equal to the sum of the squares of the other two sides (legs).

Formula: $a^2 + b^2 = c^2$

quadrilateral: a polygon with four sides.

quotient: the answer to a division problem (other than a remainder).

radius: a segment from the center of a circle to a point on that circle.

Example: 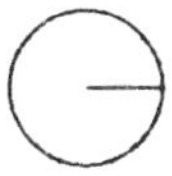

random sample: a population sample where each member of a population is equally likely to be chosen and where each member is chosen independently of any other member.

rate: when x and y are different quantities, then $\frac{x}{y}$ is the amount of x per y.

ratio: the quotient of two numbers that are in the same units. Written $n : m$ or $\frac{n}{m}$.

rational number: a number that can be written as the ratio of two integers (a fraction).

ray: a line that consists of an endpoint and all the points of a line on one side of the endpoint.

real number: any number that can be represented as a terminating, repeating, or infinite decimal.

reciprocal: the reciprocal of a number, n, is $\frac{1}{n}$. The product of any number and its reciprocal is 1.

reflection: a transformation in which each point is mapped onto its reflection image over a line. A reflection figure and its image are congruent.

remainder: the number that is left over when a number cannot be divided evenly.

Example: if you divide 7 by 3, the answer is 2 with a "remainder of 1."

rhombus: a quadrilateral with four equal sides.

right angle: an angle measuring 90 degrees.

right triangle: a triangle that has one right angle.

rounding: expressing a quantity as its nearest multiple of ten. Numbers 1-4 are rounded down. Number 5-9 are rounded up.

Example: 32 rounded to the nearest ten is 30.

Example: 37 rounded to the nearest ten is 40.

sale price: a price that is lower than the original price for an item.

sales tax: an amount of money added to the price of an item that is paid to the government.

sequence: an ordered list.

set: a group of items.

slope: (also called *tilt*) is the ratio of the $\frac{rise}{run}$ of a line. The formula for slope, m, is $m = \frac{y_2 - y_1}{x_2 - x_1}$

solution: a value for a variable that makes a number sentence (equation) true.

square: a figure with 4 right angles and 4 equal sides.

square root: $\sqrt{\ }$ a number that when multiplied by itself will produce a certain number.

Example: the square root of 25 is 5.

standard form: the way in which numbers are usually written.

Example: 6,852

sum: the answer to an addition problem.

supplementary angle: two angles with a sum of 180°.

tip: an amount of money paid to a person such as a wait person to say "thank-you" for good service, usually determined as a percentage of the total bill.

transformation: is a change. A reflection, rotation, and translation results in a change where the preimage and the image are congruent. A size change results in a change where the image is larger or smaller than the preimage.

translation: (also called a *slide*) is a horizontal move of h units and a vertical move of v units. A translation image and its image are congruent.

trapezoid: a quadrilateral with one pair of opposite sides parallel.

Example: 

triangle: a polygon with 3 sides.

value: the worth of a number.

variable: a symbol that can be replaced by another.

volume: the amount of space occupied by an object, expressed in cubic units.

Formula: length x width x height

whole number: any number 0, 1, 2, 3, etc.

6th Grade — Lesson 1

① (2)63(7) + 3(0)49 = 5786

② a. $\frac{3}{10} \div \frac{3}{4} =$; $\frac{3}{10} \times \frac{4}{3} = \frac{2}{5}$ (circled)
b. $5\frac{1}{2} \times 2\frac{1}{3} =$; $\frac{11}{2} \times \frac{7}{3} = \frac{77}{6} = 12\frac{5}{6}$ (circled)

③ a. 700 × 30 = (21000) b. 700 × 60 = (42000)

④ −7 + 7 = (0)

⑤ 4 + 3 × 2 − 2 = 4 + 6 − 2 = (8)

⑥ 12 ÷ 3 × 4 = 4 × 4 = 16

⑦ Susan: 4 × 6 = 24 oz. = 1 lb. 8 oz. = $1\frac{1}{2}$ lb.
Isabel: $1\frac{1}{4}$ lb. (Susan has more)

⑧ a. (.6) b. (.59) c. (.586)

⑨ a. (−5 and −6) b. (−6)

⑩ 7000 is (1000 times larger)

⑪ a. $6\frac{2}{3} = 6\frac{4}{6}$; $+2\frac{1}{6} = 2\frac{1}{6}$; $8\frac{5}{6}$ (circled)
b. $7 = 6\frac{8}{8}$; $-2\frac{3}{8} = 2\frac{3}{8}$; $4\frac{5}{8}$ (circled)

⑫ Answers will vary. Ex: Honda Accord, 2009 $15,500
6% sales tax: 1.06 × 15500 = $16,430

⑬ $\frac{\text{Books}}{\text{Child}} = \frac{960 \text{ books}}{120 \text{ children}} = \frac{8 \text{ books}}{\text{child}}$ (circled)

6th Grade — Lesson 2

① a. $2\frac{3}{4} \div 6 =$; $\frac{11}{4} \times \frac{1}{6} = \frac{11}{24}$ (circled)
b. $1\frac{5}{8} \times 4\frac{1}{3}$; $\frac{13}{8} \times \frac{13}{3} = \frac{169}{24} = 7\frac{1}{24}$ (circled)

② a. (3, 6, 9, 12) b. (4, 8, 12, 16) c. (12)

③ Answers will vary. Ex: 4 quarters in a dollar / $17 ÷ .25 (quarters)
4 × 17 = 68 ; $q = \frac{17}{.25} = 68$

④ a. $\frac{\text{hours}}{\text{lawn}} = \frac{9 \text{ hours}}{4 \text{ lawns}}$
b. $\frac{9}{4} = \frac{x \text{ hours}}{6}$; 4x = 54 ; x = (13.5 hours)

⑤ a. $\frac{11}{16} = \frac{11}{16}$; $-\frac{3}{8} = \frac{6}{16}$; $\frac{5}{16}$ (circled)
b. $5\frac{2}{3} = 5\frac{4}{6}$; $-2\frac{1}{6} = 2\frac{1}{6}$; $3\frac{3}{6} = 3\frac{1}{2}$ (circled)

⑥ 62.300 − 0.087 = (62.213)

⑦ a. $\frac{\text{walnuts}}{\text{choc. chips}} = \frac{2}{3}$
b. $\frac{2}{3} = \frac{3}{x}$; 9 = 2x ; (4.5 cups of choc. chips = x)

⑧ Answers will vary. Ex: $\frac{3}{4} = \frac{6}{8} = \frac{9}{12} = \frac{12}{16}$

⑨ 20) 34960 = (1748 people)
20
149
140
96
80
160

⑩ Answers will vary.

⑪ $\frac{\text{chaperones}}{\text{students}}$; $\frac{4}{15} = \frac{x}{180}$; 15x = 720 ; x = (48 chaperones)

6th Grade — Lesson 3

① about 300 × 50 = 15000, so 295 × 50 ≈ (15000)

② $\frac{7}{12} = \frac{14}{24}$ $\frac{3}{4} = \frac{18}{24}$ $\frac{11}{24}$ $\frac{2}{3} = \frac{16}{24}$
($\frac{11}{24}$ $\frac{7}{12}$ $\frac{2}{3}$ $\frac{3}{4}$)

③ b. (24, 36, 48) c. (12, 24, 60)

④ a. 80 billion
b. 80,000,000,000 (8.0×10^{10})

⑤ a. $\frac{1}{3} = \frac{33}{100}$; 99 ≠ 100
b. $\frac{1}{2} = \frac{8}{16}$; (16 = 16)
c. $\frac{4}{5} = \frac{21}{25}$; 105 ≠ 100
d. $\frac{5}{6} = \frac{15}{18}$; (90 = 90)

⑥ a. (a ∥ b) b. (d ⊥ a) or (d ⊥ b) c. (x)

⑦ 92) 5622 = 61 $\frac{10}{92}$ = ($61\frac{5}{46}$) or 92) 5622 = (61 r 10)
552
102
92
10

⑧ $2^0 = 1$ $2^1 = 2$ $2^2 = 4$ $2^3 = 8$
$2^4 = 16$ $2^5 = 32$ $2^6 = 64$ $2^7 = 128$
$2^8 = 256$ $2^9 = 512$ $2^{10} = 1024$

⑨ a. 3x − 4 = (−12) b. 3 + (−4) = (−1) c. 3 − (−4) = 3 + 4 = (7)
d. $(-4)^2$ = (16)

⑩ a. .25 = (25%) b. .5 = (50%) c. $\frac{65}{100}$ = (65%)
d. $\frac{3}{4}$ = .75 = (75%) e. $.\overline{3}$ = ($33\frac{1}{3}$%) f. 1.0 = (100%)

⑪ A = lw
A = 3 × $\frac{1}{2}$ = ($\frac{3}{2}$ in^2)

6th Grade — Lesson 4

① a. (2x + 7) b. (x − 8) c. ($x^2 - 2$)

② $2\frac{1}{2} \div 5$ means each will receive ($\frac{1}{5}$) of the fudge.
$\frac{5}{2} \times \frac{1}{5}$ = ($\frac{1}{2}$ pound per person)

③ (A ≈ −.7) (B = −.5) (C ≈ .3)

④ a. (2^3) b. ($(-3)^2$) must use parentheses; -3^2 according to order of operations: means square first, then take opposite c. (y^5)

⑤ (6 dimes and 3 nickels)

⑥ a. $\frac{4}{9} \times \frac{3}{4} = \frac{1}{3}$ (circled) b. $1\frac{2}{3} \div \frac{1}{3} = \frac{5}{3} \times \frac{3}{1} = 5$ (circled)

⑦ 95 × 60% = 95 × .6 = (57 pounds)

⑧ coins − 12 + 7 = 39 39 + 5 = (44 coins)

⑨ $7\frac{3}{4} - 3\frac{1}{2} = 4\frac{1}{4}$ (circled)

⑩ 750 × .13 = $97.50 400 × .13 = $52
(For May, use plan A; For June, use plan B)

⑪ (1, 24, 2, 12, 3, 8, 4, 6)

⑫ (12) 4 → 2, 2 6 → 2, 3 $2^2 \times 3 = 12$
or: multiples of 4, 4, 8, (12), 16, 20, 24
multiples of 6, 6, (12), 18, 24

① $-(-3) = ③$ ② $7-(-2)$; $7+2=⑨$ ③ $-(-2)^2$; $-(4) = (-4)$ ④ $8-2(-2) =$; $8+4 = (12)$

⑤ a. $\frac{1}{3} = .3\bar{3} =$ (33⅓% or 33⅓%) b. $\frac{1}{4} =$ (.25 = 25%)

c. $\frac{1}{10} =$ (.1 = 10%) d. $\frac{17}{10} =$ (1.7 = 170%)

e. $\frac{9}{100} =$ (.09 = 9%) f. $\frac{39}{100} =$ (.39 = 39%)

⑥ (5:10) (6:20)

⑦ Remember (x, y)
A = (2, 3) B = (4, −2) C = (−2, −5) D(−4, 1)

⑧ $\frac{1}{3} \times 899 \approx \frac{1}{3} \times 900 =$ (300)

⑨ a. 30 → ③, 10 → ②, ⑤: (3 × 2 × 5) b. 36 → ②, 18 → ②, 9 → ③, ③: ($2^2 \times 3^2$) c. 27 → ③, 9 → ③, ③: (3^3)

⑩ a. (30,246) b. (207,003)

⑪ a. 3 inches = $\frac{3}{12}$ = ($\frac{1}{4}$ feet) b. 10 inches = $\frac{10}{12}$ = ($\frac{5}{6}$ feet)
c. 18 inches = $\frac{18}{36}$ = ($\frac{1}{2}$ yard) d. 2 feet = ($\frac{2}{3}$ yard)

⑫ Increase of 20% means 100% + 20% = 120%
120% × 10 = 1.2 × 10 = 12 words per minute.
Increase of 25% means 100% + 25% = 125%
125% × 12 = 1.25 × 12 = 15 words per minute.

⑬ 32) 9826 = (307 r. 2)
96
226
224
2

⑭ (4)

① a. 2.32 × 4.1: 232, 928, (9.512) b. 30.5 × .2 = (6.10)

② 2.190, 2.910, 2.900, 2.099, 2.010
(2.01, 2.099, 2.19, 2.9, 2.91)

③ 253 ÷ 50 ≈ 250 ÷ 50 = ⑤

④ a. (0, 4) (1, 3) (2, 2) b.

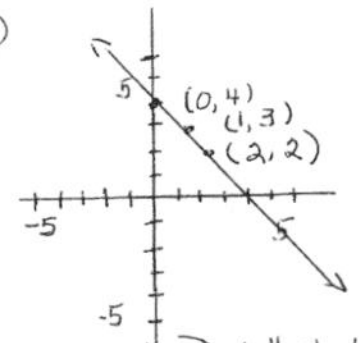

c. ex (3, 1)
3 + 1 = 4 ✓

⑤ How many groups of $\frac{3}{4}$ are in $6\frac{1}{4}$?
$6\frac{1}{4} \div \frac{3}{4} = \frac{25}{4} \times \frac{4}{3} = \frac{25}{3} = 8$ or ⅓
She can make (8 doll dresses.)

What does the ⅓ represent? Is it ⅓ yd. fabric? No. It is ⅓ of what is needed to make a dress.
$\frac{1}{3} \times \frac{3}{4} = \frac{1}{4}$ yd. fabric

⑥ (3 and 4)

⑦ 4.6) 68.110 = 14.806 ≈ (14.81)
46
221
184
371
368
300
276

⑧ a. 20 − 8 = (12 pounds)
b. Age 2 – 25 pounds
Age 3 – 35 pounds
140% × 25 = 1.4 × 25 = 35 pounds
(From age 2 to age 3)

⑨ a. $6 = 5\frac{8}{8}$; $-3\frac{3}{8} = 3\frac{3}{8}$; ($2\frac{5}{8}$) b. $3\frac{3}{5} = 3\frac{6}{10}$; $+4\frac{1}{10} = 4\frac{1}{10}$; $7\frac{5}{10} = (7\frac{1}{2})$

⑩ a. 6, 10, 14, ⑱ ㉒ ㉖ (plus 4)
b. (42)

⑪ 234.81 + 23481. = (23715.81)

⑫ a. .232 > .2318 b. $\frac{4}{5} < \frac{5}{6}$
c. $\frac{1}{3} > .3$ d. −2 > −3
e. 1.5 = 1.50 f. 200% = 2

① a. $\frac{3}{10} \div \frac{4}{5} = \frac{3}{10} \times \frac{5}{4} = (\frac{3}{8})$ b. $\frac{5}{6} \times \frac{1}{3} \times \frac{3}{5} = (\frac{1}{6})$

② 307(5/2)5 = 123

③ 52) = $15\frac{7}{52}$; 52 × 15: 260, 52, 780; 780 + 7 = (787)

④ 54 → ②, 27 → ③, ⑨ → ③ ③; 63 → ③, 21 → ③ ⑦; ⑨

⑤ 18

⑥ (−3.3 −3 .3 .33⅓) ($\frac{1}{3} = .\bar{3}$)

⑦ a. (113,000,000)
b. 113,000,000 = (1.13×10^8)

⑧ $A = \frac{1}{2}bh$
$\frac{1}{2}(2.6)(1.3) =$ (1.69 sq. in.)

⑨ a. 100% − 20% discount = 80%
80% × 229 = .8 × 229 = ($183.20)
b. cost (100%) + tax (6.5%) = 106.5%
106.5% × 183.20 = 1.065 × 183.20 = $195.108 = ($195.11)

⑩ a. (10 games) b. 6 + 2 + 2 + ½ (10) = (15 games)

⑪ a (90) b (330) c (150)

⑫ ($8.00)

① a. $\frac{3}{8} \div \frac{1}{3} = \frac{3}{8} \times \frac{3}{1} = \frac{9}{8} = (1\frac{1}{8})$ b. $3\frac{1}{2} \div \frac{1}{4} = \frac{7}{2} \times \frac{4}{1} = (14)$

② a. 2 + 3 × 4 ⓶ 2 × 3 + 4 ; 2 + 12 | 6 + 4 ; 14 | 10 (>)
b. 3 × 3 − 2 (>) 3 × (3 − 2) ; 9 − 2 | 3 × 1 ; 7 | 3
c. 6 − 2 × 3 (=) 2 × 3 − 6 ; 6 − 6 | 6 − 6 ; 0 | 0
d. 3 − (3 + 3) (<) 3 + (3 − 3) ; 3 − 6 | 3 + 0 ; −3 | 3

③ a. 30% × n = 6 or (.3n = 6) b. $\frac{.3n}{.3} = \frac{6}{.3}$ (n = 20)

④ a. |−5| = ⑤ b. |2 − 5| = |−3| = ③ c. |2| − |−5| = 2 − 5 = (−3)

⑤ $\frac{98+100+88+89+95+90}{6} = 93.\bar{3}$ (93)

⑥ a. (86200) b. (.00268) ⑦ (b, c)

⑧ a. $\frac{3}{4} =$ (.75) b. $\frac{1}{3} =$ ($.\bar{3}$) c. $\frac{2}{5} =$ (.4)

⑨ a. x + 7 = 3; + −7 + −7; (x = −4) b. x + (−8) = 5; + 8 + 8; (x = 13) c. $x + \frac{2}{3} = \frac{1}{4} = \frac{3}{12}$; $-\frac{2}{3}\ -\frac{2}{3} = \frac{-8}{12}$; $x = (\frac{-5}{12})$

⑩ −.21 $-\frac{1}{4}$ −.201 −17% $-\frac{3}{10}$
−.21 −.25 −.201 −.17 −.3
−.3 −.25 −.21 −.201 −17%
$-\frac{3}{10}$ $-\frac{1}{4}$ −.21 −.201 −17%

① a. $8\frac{2}{3} = 8\frac{6}{9}$, $-7\frac{1}{9} = 7\frac{1}{9}$, answer $1\frac{5}{9}$

b. $4\frac{1}{4} = 4\frac{3}{12}$, $+3\frac{5}{12} = 3\frac{5}{12}$, $7\frac{8}{12} = 7\frac{2}{3}$

c. $5\frac{1}{5} = 5\frac{2}{10} = 4\frac{12}{10}$, $-1\frac{3}{10} = 1\frac{3}{10} = 1\frac{3}{10}$, answer $3\frac{9}{10}$

② 30: 3, 10 → 2, 5; 45: 3, 15 → 3, 5; 90: 3, 30 → 3, 10 → 2, 5; $3 \times 5 = 15$

③ $A = s^2$; $\frac{1}{4} = s^2$; $S = \frac{1}{2}$ mi

④ $29\overline{)3012} \approx 30\overline{)3000}$ = 100

⑤ a. $20 + n < 25$
b. $2a > 10$
c. $m > 90$

⑥ $4 \times 17 \times 25 = 4 \times 25 \times 17 = 1700$

⑦ 345; $3 + 4 + 5 = 12$

⑧ a. .265, .268, .271
b. .003

⑨ a. 2000 cm = 20 m b. 3000 g = 3 Kg
c. 100 mm = 10 cm d. 4000 mL = 4 L

⑩ a. right b. straight c. obtuse d. acute

⑪ $A = \pi r^2$ $\pi \approx 3.14$
$A = 3.14(2.1^2) = 13.8474 \approx$ 13.8 sq. inches

① a. $2.35 \times 100 = 235$ b. $.005 \times .01 = .00005$ c. $4329 \times .0001 = .4329$

② Method 1: You know there are 10 dimes in a dollar, so
$8 \times 10 + 7 = 87$ dimes
Method 2: A dime is $\frac{1}{10}$ of a dollar. How many $\frac{1}{10}$'s in \$8.70?
$8.70 \div .10 = 87$ dimes

③ $8 \times 1.41 = \$11.28$
\$11.00 US is the better deal.

④ $\frac{5}{10}$, $\frac{7}{14}$, $\frac{10}{20}$

⑤ a. $3(1.59) + 3x = 7.74$
b. $4.77 + 3x = 7.74$
$-4.77 \quad -4.77$
$\frac{3x}{3} = \frac{2.97}{3}$
$x = \$.99$ for one order of fries

⑥ $A = bh$
$A = 4.5 \times 3.5 = 15.75\ cm^2$

⑦ a. $10^0 = 1$ $10^1 = 10$ $10^2 = 100$
$10^3 = 1{,}000$ $10^4 = 10{,}000$ $10^5 = 100{,}000$
$10^6 = 1{,}000{,}000$ $10^7 = 10{,}000{,}000$

b. n

⑧ 10

⑨ 22 $2 + 2 = 4$ $2 \times 2 = 4$

⑩ a. Ex (1, 3) (0, 0) (-1, -3)

b

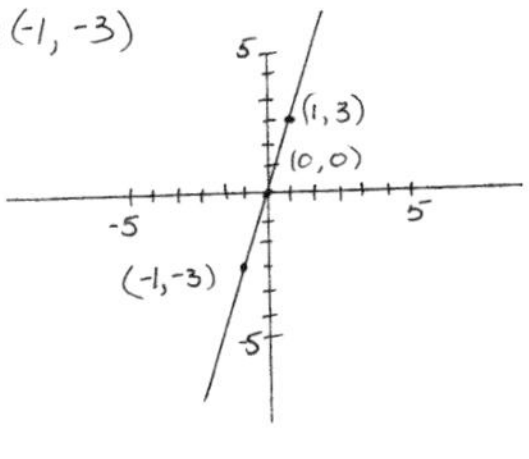

c. slope = $\frac{3}{1}$

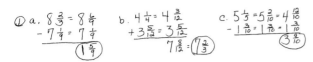

① a. $426 \div 3.3 =$ 129 r.3
$3.3\overline{)426.0}$
33
96
66
300
297
3

b. $.008 \div .04$ = .2
$.04\overline{).008}$
8
0

② a. $\frac{\text{ounces}}{\text{minute}}$ $\frac{1.6 \text{ ounces}}{1 \text{ min}}$

b. $\frac{1.6 \text{ ounces}}{1 \text{ min}} \cdot \frac{60 \text{ min}}{1 \text{ hr}} = \frac{96 \text{ ounces}}{1 \text{ hr.}}$

c. Convert 12 gallons to ounces. Both rates will be $\frac{\text{ounces}}{\text{hours}}$
$12 \times 128 = 1536$ ounces
Proportion: $\frac{96 \text{ ounces}}{1 \text{ hr}} = \frac{1536 \text{ ounces}}{x \text{ hours}}$
$\frac{1536}{96} = \frac{96x}{96}$
$x = 16$ hours

③ T

④ 3 Km = 3000 m = 300,000 cm = 3,000,000 m.m.

⑤ $584 - 396 = 188$

⑥ $-35 - (-16) = -19$ or a 19 degree difference

⑦ Divide $2\frac{1}{2}$ by $\frac{2}{3}$. You want to know how many groups of $\frac{2}{3}$ are in $2\frac{1}{2}$.
$2\frac{1}{2} \div \frac{2}{3} = \frac{5}{2} \times \frac{3}{2} = \frac{15}{4} =$ 3 full servings with $\frac{3}{4}$ serving left over.
(Recall $r = \frac{3}{4}$ means $\frac{3}{4}$ of a $\frac{2}{3}$ helping. $\frac{3}{4} \times \frac{2}{3} = \frac{1}{2}$)

⑧ $\frac{\text{successes}}{\text{shots}} = \frac{31}{48} \approx .6458$ or 64.6% or 65%

⑨ 93,000,000 = 9.3×10^7

⑩ a.

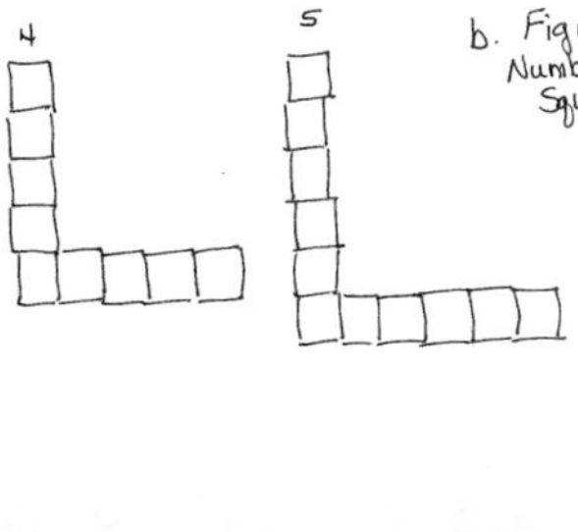

b.

Figure	4	5
Number of Squares	9	11

c. 13

① $2 - 3 \times 4^2 =$
$2 - 3 \times 16 =$
$2 - 48 = -46$

② $\frac{4-3}{6-2} = \frac{1}{4}$
(The fraction bar is a symbol of grouping.)

③ $(2+3) + 6 \div 2 =$
$5 + 6 \div 2 =$
$5 + 3 = 8$

④ a. $12 \div \frac{3}{4} =$
$12 \times \frac{4}{3} = 16$

b. $12 \times \frac{3}{4} = 9$

⑤ a. $\frac{1}{20}$ b. $\frac{1}{5}$ c. $\frac{1}{2}$

⑥ .0668 .0670 .0675 .0682

⑦ $1^2 = 1$ $2^2 = 4$ $3^2 = 9$ $4^2 = 16$
$5^2 = 25$ $6^2 = 36$ $7^2 = 49$ $8^2 = 64$
$9^2 = 81$ $10^2 = 100$ $11^2 = 121$ $12^2 = 144$

⑧ a. 10,000,000,000,000
b. 1.0×10^{13}

⑨ $\approx 25 \times 3 = 75$

⑩ a. $\frac{\text{sugar}}{\text{flour}} = \frac{2}{3}$

b. $\frac{2}{3} = \frac{1}{x}$
$1 \times 3 = 2x$
$\frac{3}{2} = \frac{2x}{2}$
$x = 1.5$ ($1\frac{1}{2}$ c. flour)

c. $\frac{3 \text{ c. flour}}{24 \text{ brownies}} = \frac{x \text{ c. flour}}{60}$
$24x = 180$
$x = 7.5$
($7\frac{1}{2}$ c. flour)

⑪ a. $\frac{1}{2}$ b. $\frac{3}{2}$ c. $-\frac{1}{5}$

d. $n \times \frac{1}{n} = 1$
$2 \times \frac{1}{2} = 1$
$\frac{3}{2} \times \frac{2}{3} = 1$
$-\frac{1}{5} \times -5 = 1$

⑫ $A = \frac{1}{2}h(b_1 + b_2)$
$A = \frac{1}{2}(\frac{1}{3})(\frac{2}{3} + 1\frac{1}{3})$
$= \frac{1}{2}(\frac{1}{3})(2) = \frac{1}{3}$ ft.^{2}

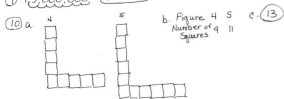

$\frac{2}{3} + 1\frac{1}{3} = \frac{2}{3} + \frac{4}{3} = \frac{6}{3} = 2$

(1) $\frac{1}{3}x = \frac{2}{3}$; $3 \times \frac{1}{3}x = \frac{2}{3}(3)$; $x = (2)$

(2) $4x = \frac{4}{7}$; $\frac{1}{4} \times 4x = \frac{4}{7} \times \frac{1}{4}$; $x = (\frac{1}{7})$

(3) $-3x = 4$; $-\frac{1}{3} \times -3x = 4 \times -\frac{1}{3}$; $x = (\frac{-4}{3})$

(4) $.05\overline{)3.675}$ = (73.5); 35, 17, 15, 25

(5) $\frac{120}{200} = \frac{60}{100} = \frac{30}{50} = \frac{15}{25}$

(6) a. 42 → 2, 21 → 3, 7; 2, 3, 7 b. (3)

(7) a. $p \times 30 = 16$; $30p = 16$ b. $\frac{30p}{30} = \frac{16}{30} = .53\overline{3} = (53.3\%)$

(8) $-\frac{13}{18}$; $-\frac{5}{6} = -\frac{15}{18}$; $-\frac{2}{3} = -\frac{12}{18}$; $-\frac{7}{9} = -\frac{14}{18}$; ($-5/6$, $-7/9$, $-13/18$, $-2/3$)

(9) (29)

(10) a. $\frac{47.25}{9} = (\$5.25)$ b. $13 \times 5.25 = (\$68.25)$

(11) a. One length and one width is half of the perimeter.
Half of 30 = 15 ft; $15 = 14\frac{2}{2}$; $-8\frac{1}{2} = -8\frac{1}{2}$; ($6\frac{1}{2}$ ft.)
b. $A = lw$; $A = 8\frac{1}{2} \times 6\frac{1}{2}$; $\frac{17}{2} \times \frac{13}{2} = \frac{221}{4} = (55\frac{1}{4}$ sq. ft.)

(12) a. $\frac{89+94+65+100+98}{5} = \frac{446}{5} = (89.2)$
b. 65 89 (94) 98 100
c. Answers will vary. (You could use the median score and give her A-)

(1) $3x - 2 = 5$; $+2 \; +2$; $\frac{1}{3} \cdot 3x = 7 \cdot \frac{1}{3}$; ($x = \frac{7}{3}$ or $2\frac{1}{3}$)

(2) $-5x + \frac{1}{2} = 6$; $+-\frac{1}{2} \; +-\frac{1}{2}$; $-\frac{1}{5} \cdot -5x = 5\frac{1}{2} = \frac{11}{2} \cdot -\frac{1}{5}$; ($x = \frac{-11}{10}$ or $-1\frac{1}{10}$)

(3) $\frac{3}{4}x + 2 = 11$; $+-2 \; +-2$; $\frac{4}{3} \cdot \frac{3}{4}x = 9 \cdot \frac{4}{3}$; ($x = 12$)

(4) $44\overline{)220}$ = 5

(5) a. 5.87(6) b. .96(1) c. (-2) d. (0)

(6) a. $5 \div 1\frac{3}{8}$; $5 \times \frac{8}{11} = \frac{40}{11} = (3\frac{7}{11})$ b. $1\frac{2}{5} \times 2\frac{1}{4}$; $\frac{7}{5} \times \frac{9}{4} = \frac{63}{20} = (3\frac{3}{20})$

(7) 531 is about 540 miles; $540 \div 60 =$ (9 hrs.)

(8) 90% of 30 = 27 questions

(9) ($3n > 10 + n$)

(10) (b. 1 meter)

(11) a. see diagram b.
c. (right triangle)
d. $A = \frac{1}{2}bh$ $b = 6$, $h = 7$; $\frac{1}{2}(6)(7) = (21 \text{ units}^2)$

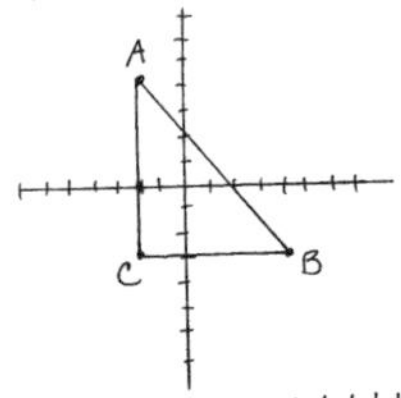

(12) $\frac{\text{miles}}{\text{day}} = \frac{30{,}000{,}000}{15 \cdot 30} = \frac{30{,}000{,}000}{450} = \frac{66666.\overline{6} \text{ miles}}{\text{day}}$

(13) $0(5-0)=0$; $1(5-1) \neq 0$; $2(5-2) \neq 0$; $3(5-3) \neq 0$; $4(5-4) \neq 0$; $5(5-5)=0$
TRUE ($x=0$)
TRUE ($x=5$)

(1) $.005\overline{)10.387}$ = (2077 R2); 10, 038, 35, 37, 35, 2

(2) $43.2 \div 2.4$; $2.4\overline{)43.2}$ = (18); 24, 192, 192

(3) 6:02 + 1 hr. = 7:02 + 45 min. = 7:47 + 10 min. slower 7:57 You have (3 minutes) to spare.

(4) a. $\frac{6}{29} = .207$ +.007 b. .19 −.01 c. = (20.1%) = .201 +.001

(5) Ivan's rate $\frac{5 \text{ cars}}{9 \text{ hours}}$; $\frac{5}{9} = \frac{x}{27}$; $\frac{9}{9}x = \frac{135}{9}$; ($x = 15$ cars)

(6) Example: How many $\frac{1}{2}$ cup servings of ice cream are in $4\frac{1}{4}$ cups of ice cream?

(7) $(-2)^2 = 4$ True ($x = -2$); $(-1)^2 \neq 4$; $0^2 \neq 4$; $1^2 \neq 4$; $2^2 = 4$ True ($x = 2$)

(8) $.15 \times 10 \times 10 = (\$15)$

(9) a. $2n + 5 = -4$ b. $2n + 5 = -4$; $+-5 \; +-5$; $\frac{1}{2} \cdot 2n = -9 \cdot \frac{1}{2}$; ($n = \frac{-9}{2}$ or $-4\frac{1}{2}$)

(10)

(11) $A = lw$; $\frac{4}{3} \cdot \frac{2}{3} = \frac{3}{4}w \cdot \frac{4}{3}$; ($\frac{8}{9}$ mi = w)

(12) $4\frac{1}{4} \times 25$; $\frac{17}{4} \times 25 = \frac{425}{4} = (106\frac{1}{4}$ mile)

(1) a. $|-2| = (2)$ b. $-|-2| = (-2)$ c. $-2^2 = (-4)$ d. $(-2)^2 = (4)$
NOTE: order of operations powers first.

(2) a. 24 in. = (2) ft. b. 64 oz = (4) lb.
c. 12 ft. = (4) yd. d. 6 qts. = ($1\frac{1}{2}$) gal.

(3) a. $30 = p \times 80$; $30 = 80p$ b. $\frac{30}{80} = \frac{80p}{80}$; $.375 = p$; ($p = 37.5\%$)

(4) a. h = 1 2 3 4 5; w = 7.00 14.00 21.00 28.00 35.00 b. $w = 7h$.
c. NOTE: connecting points is optional.
d. \$56.00

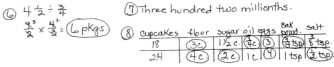

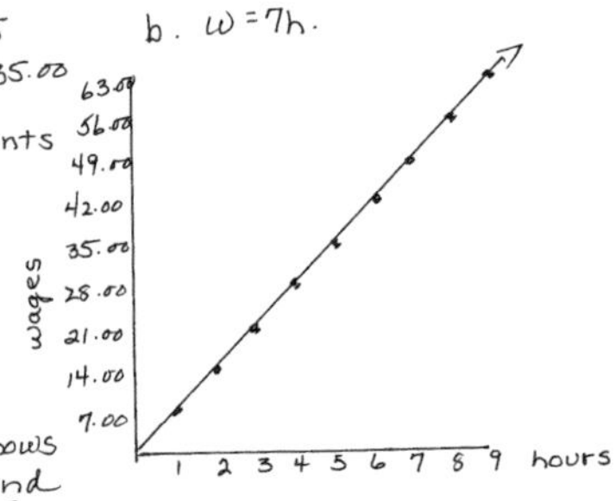

(5) a. 768000 b. 768400
c. 768424.0
d. 768423.97
NOTE: The inclusion of zero shows that the number is rounded and accurate to the nearest tenth (c) and hundredth (d).

(6) $4\frac{1}{2} \div \frac{3}{4}$; $\frac{9}{2} \times \frac{4}{3} =$ (6 pkgs)

(7) Three hundred two millionths.

(8)

cupcakes	flour	sugar	oil	eggs	Bak prod.	salt
18	(3c)	$1\frac{1}{2}$ c.	($\frac{3}{4}$c.)	(3)	($\frac{3}{4}$ tsp)	$\frac{3}{8}$ tsp.
24	(4c)	(2c)	1c	(4)	1 tsp	($\frac{1}{2}$ tsp.)

(9) $\frac{1 \text{ head}}{4 \text{ feet}}$ dog $\frac{1 \text{ head}}{2 \text{ feet}}$ bird (6 dogs 2 birds)

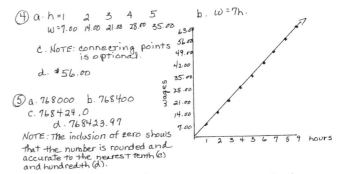

6th Grade — Lesson 17

① $\frac{3}{4} + \frac{2}{3} \div \frac{1}{6} =$ *Remember order of operations!

$\frac{3}{4} + \frac{2}{3} \times \frac{6}{1} =$

$\frac{3}{4} + 4 =$ ($4\frac{3}{4}$)

② $\frac{3}{4} - \frac{1}{4} \times 1\frac{1}{2} =$

$\frac{3}{4} - \frac{1}{4} \times \frac{3}{2} =$

$\frac{3}{4} - \frac{3}{8} = \frac{6}{8} - \frac{3}{8} =$ ($\frac{3}{8}$)

③ $(\frac{1}{2})^2 + \frac{3}{8} =$

$\frac{1}{4} + \frac{3}{8} =$

$\frac{2}{8} + \frac{3}{8} =$ ($\frac{5}{8}$)

④ a. (.80) b. (.75) c. (.6)

⑤ a. (.143) b. (2.00) c. (.00002)

⑥ a. 21 b. 108 pounds c. 115 pounds

d. It won't. The median will still be 115 pounds because the average of $\frac{115+115}{2} = 115$

⑦ $85-(-19) = 85+19 =$ (104°)

⑧ a. $\frac{2}{3} - \square = \frac{5}{8}$ $\frac{5}{8} = \frac{15}{24}$

$+-\frac{2}{3}$ $+-\frac{2}{3}$ $-\frac{2}{3} = \frac{-16}{24}$

$-\square = -\frac{1}{24}$ $\frac{-1}{24}$

$\frac{3}{2} - (\frac{1}{24}) = \frac{5}{8}$

b. $-.5 + \square = 1.2$

$+ -.5$ $+ -5$

$\square = .7$

$.5 + (.7) = 1.2$

⑨ a. (520) b. (325)

⑩ d rectangle $A = lw$
f square $A = s^2$
b trapezoid $A = \frac{1}{2}h(b_1+b_2)$
c circle $A = \pi r^2$
a triangle $A = \frac{1}{2}bh$
e parallelogram $A = bh$

⑪ Remember, the fraction bar is a symbol of grouping.

$(4+8)/(4-2)$

6th Grade — Lesson 18

① $\frac{3}{4}x = \frac{12}{15}$

$\frac{4}{3} \cdot \frac{3}{4}x = \frac{12}{15} \cdot \frac{4}{3} = \frac{16}{15} =$ ($1\frac{1}{15}$)

② $-2x = \frac{1}{5}$

$-\frac{1}{2} \cdot -2x = \frac{1}{5} \cdot -\frac{1}{2}$

$x =$ ($-\frac{1}{10}$)

③ $x - \frac{1}{3} = \frac{5}{6} = \frac{5}{6}$

$+\frac{1}{3}$ $+\frac{1}{3} = \frac{2}{6}$

$x = \frac{7}{6} =$ ($1\frac{1}{6}$)

④ Farenheit: $212-32 = 180°$
Celsius: $100-0 = 100°$

⑤ (34)

⑥ a. p = 1, 2, 3, 4, 5
C = 1.39, 2.78, 4.17, 5.56, 6.95

b. c = (1.39p) c. $C = 1.39 \cdot 8 =$ ($11.12)

⑦ a. 400800
b. 40.08

⑧ a. 1, 2, 4

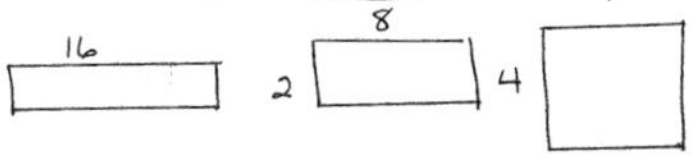

⑨ a. 1, 3

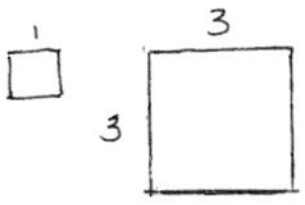

b. 4 cm and 12 cm
c. 1 cm² and 9 cm²
d. 3
e. 9

⑩ (1) 1 1 2 2 3 4 5 6 7 8 8
median is (4)

(2) Lower quartile is (2)

(3) Upper quartile is (7)

(4) IQR = (7−2 = 5)

6th Grade — Lesson 19

① (a)

② a. $\frac{3}{5} \times 2\frac{2}{5}$

$\frac{3}{5} \times \frac{12}{5} =$ ($\frac{36}{25}$ or $1\frac{11}{25}$)

b. $4\frac{1}{2} \div \frac{5}{8} =$

$\frac{9}{2} \times \frac{8}{5} =$ ($\frac{36}{5}$ or $7\frac{1}{5}$)

③ This is a rectangular prism. The sides and the bases are all rectangles.

a. Method 1 There are 6 rectangles, two of each size.
$2(8\times2)+2(8\times4)+2(2\times4) =$
$2(16)+2(32)+2(8) =$
$32+64+16 =$ (112 sq. in.)

Method 2 Notice the perimeter of the base is the length of one large rectangle, so
$p = 2+4+2+4$
$1(8\times12)+2(2\times4) =$ (112 sq. in.)

b. $V = Bh$ $B = lw$
$2\times4 = 8$
$V = 8(8) =$ (64 cubic in.)

④ d Both pairs of opposite sides are parallel.
c One pair of opposite sides is parallel.
a It has four sides.
g All angles are right angles; all sides are equal.
b Two distinct pairs of consecutive sides are equal.
e Opposite sides are equal and angles are all right angles.
f All sides are equal.

⑤ (warm)
This is almost 90°F

⑥ a. (9) b. (2)

⑦ $10 \div 1\frac{2}{3}$

$10 \times \frac{3}{5} =$ (6 boards)

⑧ (b. 75%) (d. −1.5)

⑨

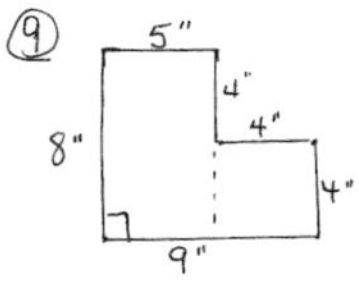

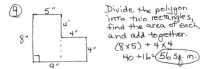

Divide the polygon into two rectangles, find the area of each, and add together.
$(8\times5) + 4\times4$
$40+16 =$ (56 sq. in.)

⑩ a.

x	0	1	2	3	4	5
y	11	8	5	2	−1	−4

b. Each "next y" is 3 less than the previous.

6th Grade — Lesson 20

① $\frac{x}{5} = \frac{9}{4}$

$\frac{45}{4} = \frac{4}{4}x$

(11.25 = x)

② $\frac{4}{15} = \frac{x}{75}$

$\frac{15x}{15} = \frac{300}{15}$

(x = 20)

③ $\frac{x}{1.5} = \frac{5}{20}$

$\frac{20x}{20} = \frac{7.5}{20}$

(x = .375)

④ $45 \times 5.00 \times .9 =$ $100\% - 10\% = 90\%$
$202.50
$225 - 202.5 =$ ($22.50 left)

⑤ a. $\frac{\$75}{6\,doz.} = \frac{\$12.50}{doz}$ b. $\frac{\$12}{doz}$ c. $\frac{\$26}{2\,doz} = \frac{\$13}{doz.}$

(STORE B)

⑥ b square kilometers
a square meters
d square centimeters
c square millimeters

⑦ Ima subtracted before she multiplied.
$8-2\times5 = 8-10 = -2$

⑧ $2n < 5+(-n)$

⑨ a. diameter b. radius c. 16 cm.

⑩ a. * * * * *
* * * * *

* * * * * *
* * * * * *

b. (20)

⑪ a. $|-4| = |4|$
4 4

b. $-4^2 < (-4)^2$
−16 16

c. $2^4 = 4^2$
16 16

d. $\frac{1}{3} > .3$
$.\overline{3}$ .3

⑫ a. $-3+(-4)+(-5) =$ (−12) b. $(-3)(-4)(-5) =$ (−60)

c. $(-4)^2 =$ (16) d. $-3+(-4)\times-5$
$-3+20 =$ (17)

① 6③ ②7 + 13 = 103

② $4986 \div 93 \approx 5000 \div 100 =$ (50)

③ a. 8.14×9.1: 814, 7326, (74.074) b. $.078 \times .02 = .00156$ (.00156)

④ $3 + 2n = 15$

⑤ a. 7 tenths b. 7 thousandths c. 7 hundredths

⑥ $100\% - 8\% = 92\%$ correct. $50 \times .92 =$ (46)

⑦ $\frac{3\text{ gal}}{1\text{ mi}} = \frac{n\text{ gal.}}{3471\text{ mi.}}$ n = (10,413 gallons)

⑧ 3 ⊕ 4 ⊖ 1 ⊕ 5 ⊖ 2 = 9

⑨ a. $1\frac{1}{3} \div 2\frac{4}{9}$; $\frac{4}{3} \times \frac{9}{22} =$ ($\frac{6}{11}$)
b. $6\frac{1}{8} \times \frac{1}{7} = \frac{49}{8} \times \frac{1}{7} =$ ($\frac{7}{8}$)

⑩ $\frac{5}{6}$ $\frac{7}{8}$ $\frac{9}{10}$ $\frac{11}{12}$

⑪ 20 → ② 10 → 2 ⑤; 30 → ② 15 → 3 ⑤ (10 guests)

⑫ $(2+4) \times 3 - 2 + 3 = 19$

⑬ She is to find how many groups of $\frac{2}{3}$ are in $2\frac{1}{2}$
$2\frac{1}{2} \div \frac{2}{3} = \frac{5}{2} \times \frac{3}{2} = \frac{15}{4} = 3\frac{3}{4}$
There are 3 full groups and $\frac{3}{4}$ of another, or $\frac{3}{4} \times \frac{2}{3} = \frac{6}{12} = \frac{1}{2}$ of a pound.
Check: $\frac{2}{3} \times 3 + \frac{1}{2} = 2 + \frac{1}{2} = 2\frac{1}{2}$

① a. $\frac{5\text{ red}}{20\text{ total}}$ b. $\frac{5}{20} = \frac{n}{100}$; $20n = 500$; (n = 25)

② $1\frac{1}{2} \div \frac{1}{6}$; $\frac{3}{2} \times \frac{6}{1} =$ (9 cakes)

③ a. $3a + 4b - a$ ($2a + 4b$) b. $2x^2 + x - x^2 + 3x^3$ ($3x^3 + x^2 + x$) c. $4x^2 + 9 + x^2 - 5$ ($5x^2 + 4$)

④ a (1.2) b (.12)

⑤ $\frac{6}{8}$ $\frac{9}{12}$

⑥ a. ABCD is congruent to WXYZ (TRUE)
b. ∠A = ∠W (TRUE)
c. ABCD is a rectangle (FALSE)
d. BC = XY (TRUE)
e. The area of ABCD = the area of WXYZ (TRUE)

⑦ $A = \frac{1}{2}bh$
$A = \frac{1}{2}(2.5)(4.3) =$ (5.375 sq. in.)

⑧ a. 3^3 b. $(\frac{1}{2})^4$ c. a^b

⑨ a. (2,1) (4,2) (0,0) b.
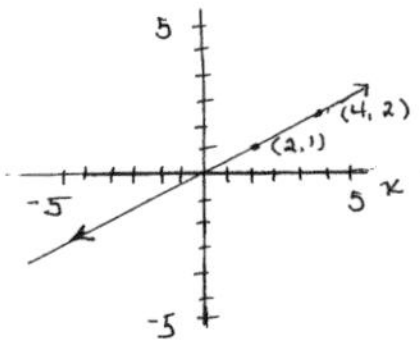

c. NO

⑩ b

⑪ $5 = p \times 20$
$\frac{5}{20} = \frac{20p}{20}$
$.25 = p$ (25%)

① a. (133) b. ($\frac{3}{4}$) c. (147) d. (80)

② a. $20\frac{3}{5} = 20\frac{6}{10}$; $-10\frac{9}{10} = -10\frac{9}{10}$; $9\frac{5}{10} =$ ($9\frac{1}{2}$)
b. $15\frac{1}{4} = 15\frac{2}{8}$; $-9\frac{3}{8} = -9\frac{3}{8}$; ($5\frac{7}{8}$)

③ a. $\frac{\$33}{22} = \frac{3}{2} =$ ($1.50 student) $\frac{\$44}{22} = \frac{4}{2} =$ ($2.00 student) b. ($.50)

④ $14\overline{)238000}$ = (17000); 14, 98, 98

⑤ 2 4 6 (2 2, 2 3) $2 \times 2 \times 3 =$ (12)

⑥ Let p = original price
80% p = 48
.8p = 48
(p = $60)
100% − 20% = 80%

⑦ a. $\frac{2+15+5+4+6}{5} =$ (6.4)
b. 2 4 ⑤ 6 15
c. They are fairly close. Probably the median. There was a high scoring game that made the mean a little high.

⑧ * * * / * * * } original $\frac{2}{5}$
* * * / * * * / * * * + $\frac{3}{5}$ more

⑨ $42\frac{1}{2}\% = .425 = \frac{425}{1000}$

⑩ $4 + 2^2 - 9 \div (2+1)$
$4 + 2^2 - 9 \div 3$
$4 + 4 - 9 \div 3$
$4 + 4 - 3$
(5)
parentheses, powers, division, addition and subtraction, Left to right

⑪ a. 400 cm = 4m.
b. 500 ml = .5L
c. 2 Km = 2000 m
d. 5 Kg = 5000 g.
e. 10 cm = 100 mm
f. 500g = .5 Kg

⑫ rectangle

① a. (6) b. (12) ② 100 times ③ 6000 times

④ a. $-5 + (-7) =$ (−12) b. $-5 - (-7) = -5 + 7 =$ (2)

⑤ $4 \div \frac{1}{4} = 4 \times 4 = 16$ $1.50 + 16 \times .45 =$ ($8.70)

⑥
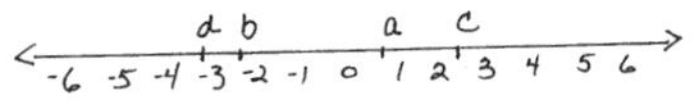

⑦ 2 2 2 3 5 10 10 10 10
a. $\frac{2+2+2+3+5+10+10+10+10}{9} = 6$
b. 2 2 2 3 ⑤ 10 10 10 10
c. 10 d. median or mean

⑧ a. $2a + 4b + c + 5a - 2b - c =$ ($7a + 2b$) b. $3x + 5x^2 - 2x$ ($x + 5x^2$)

⑨ a. $2(\frac{1}{2}) =$ (1) b. $2(-\frac{1}{2}) =$ (−1) c. $2 + \frac{1}{2} + (-2) + (-\frac{1}{2}) =$ (0)
d. $(-2)^2 =$ (4) e. $(-\frac{1}{2})^2 =$ ($\frac{1}{4}$) f. $\frac{2(\frac{1}{2})}{-2(-\frac{1}{2})} =$ (1)

⑩ a. Nancy 2(51) = 102 b. 3(17) = (51) Jeannie = (17)

⑪ a. $x^2 = 9$; x = 3 or −3; written: (±3) b. $\sqrt{x} = 5$; x = (25) c. $|x| = 2$; x = 2 or −2; (±2)

6th Grade **Lesson 25**

① $2a-(3b+2b)$
$2a-(5b)=$ (circled: $2a-5b$)

② $2x^2y-4y^2$
already simplified

③ $3(a+b)=$ (circled: $3a+3b$)

④ a. $2=\frac{2}{1}$ b. $-.3=\frac{-3}{10}$ c. $.3=\frac{1}{3}$
d. $25\%=\frac{25}{100}$ e. $-10\%=\frac{-10}{100}$ f. $.09=\frac{9}{100}$

⑤ a. $\frac{5}{8}=\frac{n}{40}$
$\frac{8n}{8}=\frac{200}{8}$
(circled: $n=25$)

b. $\frac{2}{3}=\frac{n}{24}$
$\frac{3n}{3}=\frac{48}{3}$
(circled: $n=16$)

c. $\frac{5}{6}=\frac{n}{27}$
$\frac{6n}{6}=\frac{135}{6}$
(circled: $n=22.5$)

⑥ $3.756+37.042\approx 4+37=$ (circled: 41)

⑦ a. 106% — 1.06 b. $1\frac{70}{1000}$ (circled) — 1.07 c. $\frac{103}{100}$ — 1.03 d. $\frac{110}{100}$ — 1.10

⑧ $1{,}600{,}000\times 5.5\%$
$1{,}600{,}000\times .055=\$88000$

⑨ (circled: 29)

⑩ 6 ft. 11 in.
6 ft. 11 in.
9 ft. 7 in.
9 ft. 7 in.
30 ft. 36 in. = 33 ft.

⑪ $100\%-20\%=80\%$
80% of 38.00
$.8(38)=$ (circled: \$30.40)

⑫ a. $.1n=5.50$
b. $2a<8$
c. $3n>20$

⑬ a. $2\times 6\div 3 \;\underline{=}\; 6\div 3\times 2$
$4 \qquad 4$
b. $(\frac{1}{2})^3 \;\underline{>}\; (\frac{1}{3})^2$
$\frac{1}{8} \qquad \frac{1}{9}$
c. $3-(3\div 3)\times 3 \;\underline{=}\; (3-3)\div 3\times 3$
$3-1\times 3 \qquad 0\div 9$
$0 \qquad 0$
d. $1.0^3 \;\underline{=}\; 1{,}000{,}000^0$
$1 \qquad 1$

6th Grade **Lesson 26**

① $\frac{2}{3}+3\frac{1}{2}-\frac{5}{6}=$
$\frac{2}{3}+\frac{7}{2}-\frac{5}{6}=$
$\frac{4}{6}+\frac{21}{6}-\frac{5}{6}=\frac{20}{6}=3\frac{2}{6}=3\frac{1}{3}$

② $\frac{2}{3}\div\frac{2}{9}\times\frac{1}{4}=$
$\frac{2}{3}\times\frac{9}{2}\times\frac{1}{4}=$ (circled: $\frac{3}{4}$)

③ .9 .8 2.0 3.2
NOTE: 2.0, not 2 shows rounding to nearest tenth.

④ a. 4^3 (circled: <) 3^4
$64 \qquad 81$
b. 200% (circled: =) 2
$2 \qquad 2$
c. -3^2 (circled: <) $|-9|$
$-9 \qquad 9$
d. $\frac{1}{3}$ (circled: >) 33%
$\frac{1}{3} \qquad \frac{33}{100}$
$\frac{100}{300} \qquad \frac{99}{300}$

⑤ $\frac{2}{8}=\frac{w}{20}$
$8w=40$
$w=$ (circled: 5 ft.)
$\frac{w}{l}$

⑥ $P(h)=\frac{1}{2}$ If it is a fair coin, the probability is still $\frac{1}{2}$.

⑦ $\frac{140}{28}=\frac{\nu}{70}$ $\frac{\text{chicken fingers}}{\text{students}}$
$\frac{28\nu}{28}=\frac{9800}{28}$
$\nu=$ (circled: 350 chicken fingers)

⑧ a. $3\frac{3}{4}\times 6\frac{1}{2}=$
$\frac{15}{4}\times\frac{13}{2}=\frac{195}{8}=$ (circled: $24\frac{3}{8}$)

b. $1\frac{3}{4}\div\frac{1}{8}=$
$\frac{7}{4}\times\frac{8}{1}=$ (circled: 14)

⑨ $14-0.356$
14.000
$-\ .356$
(circled: 13.644)

⑩ a. $\frac{1}{2}n+4$
b. $n-2$
c. $-n$

⑪ a. $\nu^2=49$
$\nu=$ (circled: ± 7)
b. $3^x=27$
$\nu=$ (circled: 3)
c. $|x|=9$
$\nu=$ (circled: ± 9)

⑫ a. (circled: \$4.57) b. (circled: 10)
c. (circled: 5) d. (circled: 2)
e. (circled: 7.9) f. (circled: −6)

6th Grade **Lesson 27**

① $d=rt$
$\frac{520}{8}=\frac{r\cdot 8}{8}$
(circled: 65 mph = r)

② a. $28\times 51\approx 30\times 50=$ (circled: 1500)
b. $103\times 98\approx 100\times 100=10000$

③ a. 5 pounds bounces
b. 3 gallons 3 quarts

④ $\frac{5}{6}\cdot 60=50$ min $.6(60)=36$ min.
(circled: Mary Pat)

⑤ a. 2-liter bottle $\frac{1.19}{67.2}\approx\frac{\$.0177}{\text{ounce}}$ 6-pack $6\times 12=72$
$\frac{1.50}{72}\approx\frac{\$.02}{\text{ounce}}$
b. The 2-liter bottle.

⑥ $100\%-15\%=85\%$
$85\%\times 20=.85(20)=\$17$
Half price:
$\frac{17}{2}=\$8.50$ per Widget

⑦ 
All the numbers greater than or equal to −3 and less than or equal to 3.

⑧ a. $V=5^3$
$8=5^3$ (circled: 2 units)
$2=5$
b. $6^3=$ (circled: 216 units^3)

⑨ a. $\frac{2}{7}=\frac{10}{35}$ T
$70=70$
b. $\frac{2}{3}\neq\frac{18}{24}$ F
$54\neq 48$
c. $\frac{4}{5}=\frac{48}{60}$ T
$240=240$

⑩ a. $\frac{4+8+8+10+14+16}{6}=\frac{60}{6}=10$

b. $10-4=6$ $10-8=2$ $10-8=2$
$10-10=0$ $|10-14|=4$ $|10-16|=6$

c. $\frac{6+2+2+0+4+6}{6}=\frac{20}{6}=3.\overline{3}$

6th Grade **Lesson 28**

① $8\times 1\frac{1}{2}$
$\frac{8}{1}\times\frac{3}{2}=$ (circled: 12)

② $2\frac{1}{4}\times 3\frac{1}{2}$
$\frac{9}{4}\times\frac{7}{2}=\frac{63}{8}=$ (circled: $7\frac{7}{8}$)

③ $-\frac{1}{2}\times\frac{3}{4}=$ (circled: $\frac{-3}{8}$)

④ $\frac{-2}{3}\times-\frac{5}{8}=$ (circled: $\frac{5}{12}$)

⑤ Ima forgot to convert yards to feet so that the units would be the same in her proportion. 2.5 yds $=7.5$ ft.
$\frac{.58}{1}=\frac{\nu}{7.5}$
$\nu=\$4.35$

⑥ $\frac{3}{4}\div 2=\frac{3}{4}\times\frac{1}{2}=$ (circled: $\frac{3}{8}$ c. each)

⑦ a. (circled: 225) b. (circled: 256) c. (circled: 150) d. (circled: 19)

⑧ $3\frac{1}{2}\div\frac{1}{4}$ How many $\frac{1}{4}$'s in $3\frac{1}{2}$?
$\frac{7}{2}\times\frac{4}{1}=14$ $14\times 1=$ (circled: 14 feet)

⑨ $3\times 37=$ (circled: \$111)

⑩ Is $\$7.50\div .25<30$?
$7.50\div .25=30$
You would have exactly enough.

⑪ a. 3 and $\frac{1}{3}$ R b. .01 and 100 R
c. 4 and −4 O d. $-\frac{2}{3}$ and $-\frac{3}{2}$ R

⑫ $A=\pi r^2$
$A=\pi(3^2)=$ (circled: 28.3 in.^{2})

① $5 \div \frac{1}{5} =$
$5 \times 5 = 25$ (circled)

② $2\frac{1}{2} \div 1\frac{2}{3} =$
$\frac{5}{2} \times \frac{3}{5} = \frac{3}{2} = 1\frac{1}{2}$ (circled)

③ $-\frac{3}{5} \div \frac{1}{10} =$
$\frac{-3}{5} \times 10 = -6$ (circled)

④ 7.3) 1542.0 = 211 r17 (circled)
146
82
73
90
73
17

⑤ .03) .004 = .2

⑥ a.

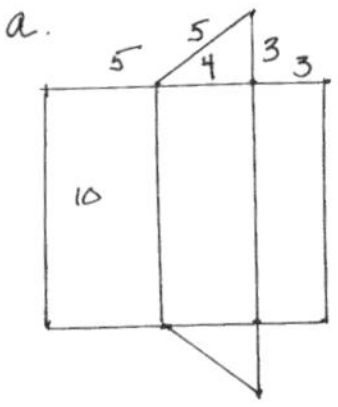

b. Method 1
$(5 \times 10) + (4 \times 10) + (3 \times 10) + 2 \cdot \frac{1}{2} 4 \cdot 3$
$50 + 40 + 30 + 12 =$
132 sq. in. (circled)
Method 2
$10 \times 12 + 2 \cdot \frac{1}{2} \cdot 3 \cdot 4$ or
$120 + 12 =$ 132 sq. in. (circled)

⑦ a. (4/3)*π*3^3
b. ≈ $113 in^3$ (circled)
c. $V = Bh$ $B = \frac{1}{2}bh$
$\frac{1}{2} \cdot 3 \cdot 4 = 6$
$V = 6 \cdot 10 = 60 in^3$ (circled)

⑧ Miles
$\frac{3 + 3.7 + 2 + 2.3 + 3}{5} = \frac{14}{5} = 2.8$ (circled)
Arianna $\frac{4 + 3 + 3.7 + 3 + 2.3}{5} = \frac{16}{5} = 3.2$ (circled)

⑨ $.25 \times 20 =$ 5 hits (circled)

⑩ a. $\frac{65 + 66 + 66 + 68 + 70}{5} = 67$ in.
b. $67 - 65 = 2$ $67 - 66 = 1$ $67 - 66 = 1$
$|67 - 68| = 1$ $|67 - 70| = 3$
$\frac{2 + 1 + 1 + 1 + 3}{5} = \frac{8}{5} = 1.6$
c. The heights average 1.6 in. in from the mean.

① $1 + 12 = 13$
$2 + 11 = 13$
$3 + 10 = 13$
$4 + 9 = 13$ $4 \times 9 = 36$
4 and 9 (circled)

② 100% + 15%
115% of 220
$1.15 \times 220 =$
253 students (circled)

③ a. $\frac{25 \text{ miles}}{2.5 \text{ hours}} = \frac{10 \text{ miles}}{\text{hour}}$ (circled)
b. $\frac{2.5 \text{ hours}}{25 \text{ miles}} = \frac{.1 \text{ hour}}{1 \text{ mile}}$ (circled)

④ a. 100
b. 20
c. 80
d. 90
e. 60
f. 90−60=30
g. 7

⑤ 81: ③ 27, ③ 9, ③ ③
54: ③ 18, ③ 6, ③ 2
36: ② 18, ② 9, ③ ③
$3 \cdot 3 = 9$ (circled)

⑥ $5375 \div 6 \approx 5400 \div 6 = 900$ (circled)

⑦ 27 (circled)

⑧ $\frac{13}{17} \approx .76$ $\frac{25}{31} \approx .81$ extra point (circled)

⑨ a. about 16 sq. units (circled)
b. about 4 (circled)
c. about $8.00 (circled)

10\. a. $30 \times 11 =$ 330 problems (circled)
b. $\frac{11 \text{ prob}}{30 \text{ min}} \approx \frac{.37 \text{ prob}}{\text{min.}}$

① a. $1 + 4^2 \times 3$
$1 + 16 \times 3$
$1 + 48 = 49$ (circled)
b. $16 - 4/2 + 3$
$16 - 2 + 3 = 17$ (circled)
c. $100/25 - 2 \times 2$
$4 - 4 = 0$ (circled)

② 50% = .5 $3^0 = 1$ π ≈ 3.14 $\frac{4}{3} = 1.\overline{3}$ −.75 $-2^2 = -4$

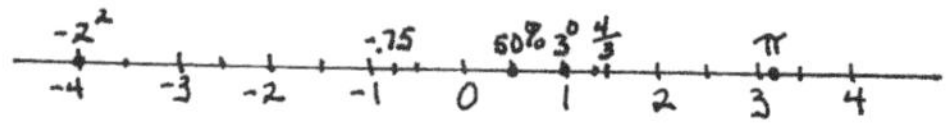

③ 1.91 1.09 1.119 1.19
1.910 1.090 1.119 1.190

1.09 1.119 1.19 1.91

④ a. $3 \times 4 + 2$ > $3 + 4 \times 2$
12+2 3+8
14 > 11
b. $2 \times 2 - 1$ > $2 \times (2 - 1)$
4−1 2×1
3 > 2
c. 1.0^3 = 10^0
1 = 1
d. $8 - (8 + 8)$ < $(8 - 8) + 8$
8−16 0+8
−8 < 8

⑤ a. $(-2)(3)(5)$
−30 (circled)
b. $(-2)^2$
4 (circled)
c. $5(-2 + 3)$
$5(1) = 5$ (circled)

⑥ $\frac{12}{15} = \frac{x}{80}$ $15x = 960$ x = 64 home runs

⑦ a.
b.

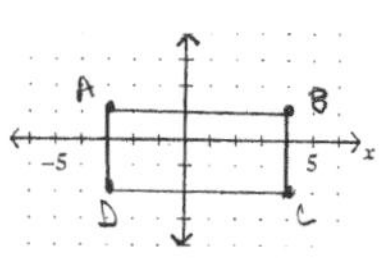

c. rectangle
d. $A = lw$
$= 7 \cdot 3 = 21 \text{ units}^2$

⑧ a. $5n$ b. $n - 8$ c. $3 + 2n$

⑨ a. 37, 45
b. 8
c. examples: add 8 to previous to get next
or Find the zero term. $5 - 8 = -3$
$t = 8n - 3$
d. $t = 8(10) - 3 = 77$

⑩ a. $\frac{40 + 81 + 86 + 88 + 93}{5} = 77.6$ mean
b. 40 81 [86] 88 93 86 median
c. $\frac{81 + 86 + 88 + 93}{4} = 87$ mean
81 [86 88] 93 $\frac{86 + 88}{2}$ 87 median
The mean was most affected by the score of 40
d. Answers will vary. A B grade would seem to best represent her effort.

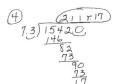

① a. $6 \div 2 + 7 \times 3$
$3 + 21 = 24$ (circled)

b. $8 + 40/{-5} - 3$
$8 + -8 - 3 = -3$ (circled)

c. $\frac{8+40}{-5-3}$
$\frac{48}{-8} = -6$ (circled)

② a. $\frac{1}{2} + \frac{1}{2} \; \underline{>} \; \frac{1}{2} \times \frac{1}{2}$
$1 > \frac{1}{4}$

b. $\frac{1}{2} \times \frac{1}{2} \; \underline{<} \; \frac{1}{2} \div \frac{1}{2}$
$\frac{1}{4} \qquad \frac{1}{2} \times 2$
$\frac{1}{4} < 1$

c. $\frac{1}{2} \times \frac{1}{2} \; \underline{=} \; \frac{1}{2} \div 2$
$\frac{1}{4} \qquad \frac{1}{2} \times \frac{1}{2}$
$\frac{1}{4} = \frac{1}{4}$

d. $\left(\frac{1}{2}\right)^2 \; \underline{=} \; \frac{1}{2} \times \frac{1}{2}$
$\frac{1}{4} = \frac{1}{4}$

③ $x + 22 > 57$

④ $\frac{3}{8} = .375 \quad \frac{1}{3} = .\overline{3}$

$\frac{1}{3} \quad .35 \quad \frac{3}{8} \quad .38$

⑤ a. $2x = 6$
$\frac{1}{2} \cdot 2x = 6 \cdot \frac{1}{2}$
$x = 3$ (circled)

b. $\frac{1}{2}x = -10$
$2 \cdot \frac{1}{2}x = -10 \cdot 2$
$x = -20$ (circled)

c. $\frac{1}{3}x + 3 = 5$
$+{-3} \quad +{-3}$
$\frac{1}{3}x = 2$
$3 \cdot \frac{1}{3}x = 2 \cdot 3$
$x = 6$ (circled)

⑥ a. examples: ∠1 and ∠3, ∠2 and ∠4
b. examples ∠1 and ∠4, ∠2 and ∠3

⑦ Let $a = 2$ Let $b = \frac{1}{2}$ Let $c = -\frac{1}{2}$ Let $d = -2$

a. (1) $\frac{1}{2}$ (2) -2 (3) $-\frac{1}{2}$ (4) 2

(4) is the largest.

b. (1) $\frac{1}{2}$ (2) $\frac{1}{4}$ (3) $-\frac{1}{4}$ (4) $\frac{1}{4}$

(3) is the smallest.

⑧ a. $x - y = 3$
$4 - 1 = 3 \quad (4, 1)$
$3 - 0 = 3 \quad (3, 0)$
$2 - (-1) = 3 \quad (2, -1)$

b.

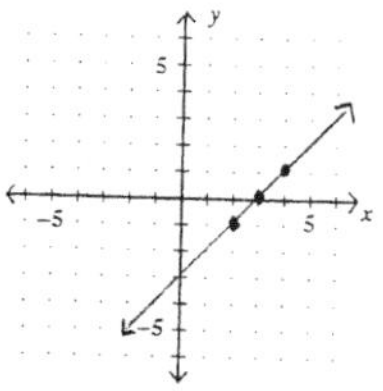

c. example: $(5, 2)$
d. $5 - 2 = 3$

⑨ a. $a + 5$
b. $a + 5 = 2a$

c. $a + 5 = 2a$
$-a \quad -a$
$5 = a$

Ann is 5
Ben is 10

⑩ a. 3 b. 7 The absolute value symbols are symbols of grouping. Evaluate 3−10 first

c. 13

⑪

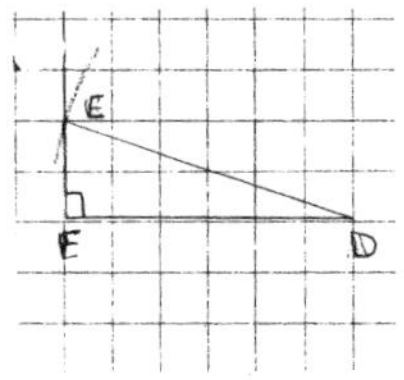

① $(8 - 6) \times 16 \div 4 = 8$

② This can be completed by folding point A onto point B. $\overleftrightarrow{CD}$ is the fold line.
If you have learned constructions then:
a) ⊙ A containing B
b) ⊙ B containing A
c) Points C and D are the intersections of ⊙A and ⊙ B.
d) $\overleftrightarrow{CD}$ is ⊥ bisector of $\overline{AB}$

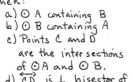

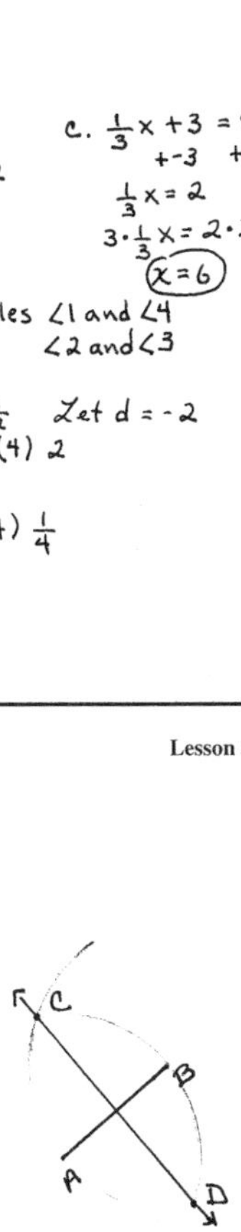

③ a. $\frac{4}{10} = \frac{10}{p} \qquad 4p = 100$
$p = 25$ turtles

b. Usually to make an accurate prediction of population more than one sample needs to be taken. The class could have sampled the population, released the turtles, waited an hour and done a second sample. Average the two samples.

④ $C = 2\pi r$
$= 2 \cdot \frac{22}{7} \cdot \frac{5}{2} = \frac{110}{7} \approx 15.7$ inches

⑤ a. 18 b. $\frac{18}{100}$ c. $\frac{1}{6}$

d. $\frac{18}{100} = .18 \qquad \frac{1}{6} \approx .16$

These numbers are pretty close. The die is probably fair.

⑥ a.

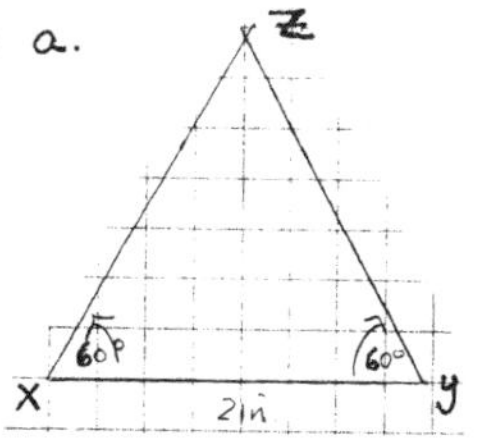

b. $m\angle Z = 60°$

c. The triangle is equilateral. All angles measure 60°; therefore, all sides are equal.

⑦ Let $x = -3$
$(-3)^2 = 9$

$-3 < 0$ but $(-3)^2 > 0$
Remember: A negative times a negative is a positive.

⑧ a. $A = bh$
$= 16.8 \cdot 5.4 = 90.72 \approx 90.7 \text{ in}^2$

b. You do not need length 6.8 in to find the area.

⑨ a. $3(x + y) = 3x + 3y$ b. $7(x + y) = 7x + 7y$

⑩ a. $2x + -4 = 12$
$+4 \quad +4$
$2x = 16$
$\frac{1}{2} \cdot 2x = 16 \cdot \frac{1}{2}$
$x = 8$ (circled)

b. $29 - x = 15$
$+{-29} \quad +{-29}$
$-x = -14$
$x = 14$ (circled)

c. $\frac{2}{3}x = \frac{1}{2}$
$\frac{3}{2} \cdot \frac{2}{3}x = \frac{1}{2} \cdot \frac{3}{2}$
$x = \frac{3}{4}$ (circled)

⑪ Let $x = \frac{1}{2}$
$\left(\frac{1}{2}\right)^2 = \frac{1}{4}$

$0 < \frac{1}{2} < 1$

$\frac{1}{4} < \frac{1}{2}$

① a. $2.3 \times 10^4 = 23000 = 23{,}000$

b. $1.0 \times 10^6 = 1000000 = 1{,}000{,}000$

② $3x + 2x - 6 + x = 180$
$6x - 6 = 180$
$+6 \quad +6$
$6x = 186$
$x = 31°$

$2x - 6 =$
$2(31) - 6 = 56°$
$3x =$
$3(31) = 93°$

③ a. Mean: $\frac{54}{10} = 5.4$

b. Median: 1 2 3 4 4 7 8 8 8 9
$\frac{4+7}{2} = \frac{11}{2} = 5.5$

c. Mode: 8

④ a. $A = \pi r^2$
$= 3.14 \cdot 3^2 \approx 28.26 \text{ in}^2$

b. Since $\pi \approx 3.14$, the answer is an approximation.

⑤ a. Distributive property
b. Commutative property
c. Associative property

⑥ a. $2x + x = 180$
b. $3x = 180$
$x = 60°$ $\quad 2x = 120°$

⑦ a. $m\angle 1 = 95°$
b. $m\angle 2 = 85°$
c. $m\angle 3 = 85°$
d. $m\angle 4 = 180 - 70 - 95 = 15°$

⑧ a. $P(10) = \frac{4}{52} = \frac{1}{13}$

b. P(jack or queen) = $\frac{1}{13} + \frac{1}{13} = \frac{2}{13}$

c. P(two aces) = $\frac{4}{52} \cdot \frac{3}{51} = \frac{1}{221}$

⑨ a. $2x + x = 90$
b. $3x = 90$
$x = 30°$ $\quad 2x = 60°$

⑩ They chose from the after school sports practices. These students favor playing sports after school, and they do not represent the entire school.

① a. No. They are all wrestlers, so they are very likely all boys.
b. No. Volunteers tend to be highly motivated to be on a committee.
c. Yes. Computers are random and attendance sheets include all students.

② a.

h =	0	1	2	3	4	5	6
w =	0	8.50	17.00	25.50	34.00	42.50	51.00

b. $w = 8.5h$

c.

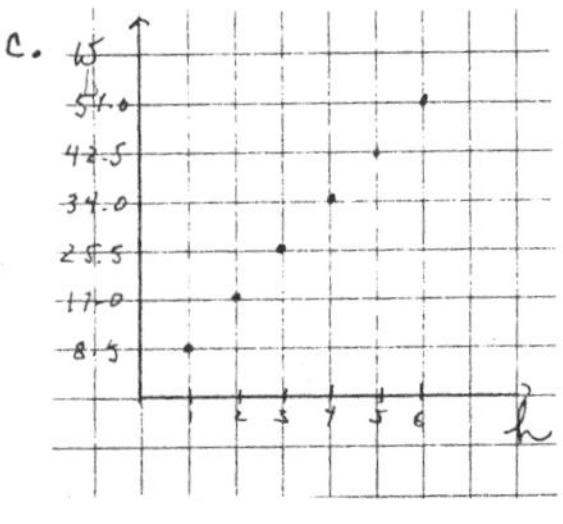

d. No, because she is probably not being paid for partial hours. If anything, there may be rounding up.

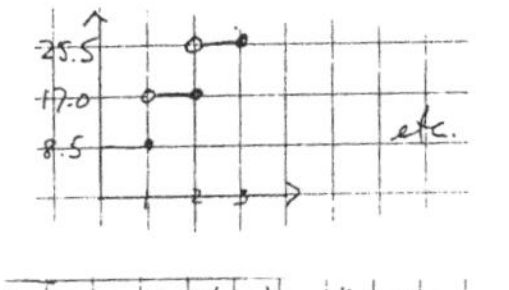

e. $w = 8.5(10) = \$85.00$

③ a. $1\frac{1}{4}, \frac{1}{2}$

b. $-\frac{3}{4}$

c. examples: previous term $- \frac{3}{4}$ = next term
or $t = -\frac{3}{4}n + 4\frac{1}{4}$

d. $t = -\frac{3}{4}(10) + \frac{17}{4} = -\frac{30}{4} + \frac{17}{4} = -\frac{13}{4} = -3\frac{1}{4}$

④

	Measure	Justification
a. $m\angle 2$	50°	∠2 is supplementary to ∠1
b. $m\angle 3$	130°	∠1 and ∠3 are vertical angles.
c. $m\angle 4$	50°	∠2 and ∠4 are vertical angles.

⑤

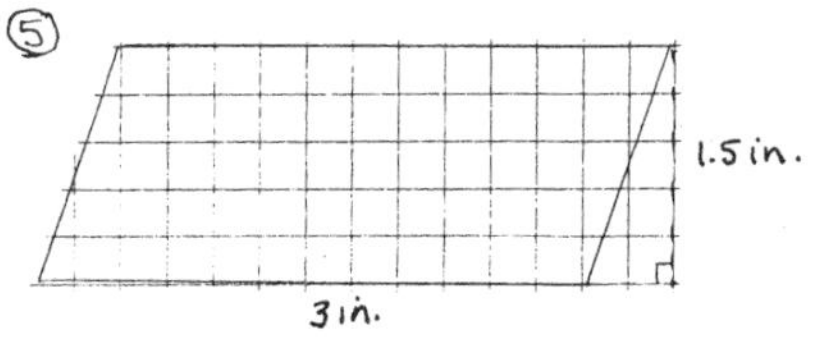

⑥ a. $4(.04 + .06)$ $\quad$ b. $4(.1) = .4$

⑦
$.034$
$\times 5.3$
$.1802$

Count places from right to left for both numbers. .034 3 places. 5.3 1 place. Count a total of 4 places.

Summer Math Skills Lesson Tracker

Book Grade Level ____________ **Name of Student** ______________________________

Lesson #	# of Problems	# of Problems Completed	# of Problems Incorrect	Parent/Tutor Initials
1				
2				
3				
4				
5				
6				
7				
8				
9				
10				
11				
12				
13				
14				
15				
16				
17				
18				
19				
20				
21				
22				
23				

Lesson #	# of Problems	# of Problems Completed	# of Problems Incorrect	Parent/Tutor Initials
24				
25				
26				
27				
28				
29				
30				
31				
32				
33				
34				
35				

Extras (Brain Aerobics, Math Facts Sharpener)

Questions	# Completed	# Correct	# Incorrect	Parent/Tutor Initials

Parent/Tutor Signature ____________________________________